D0423359

ATLANTA PUBLIC LIBRARY

73

THE STORM HAS MANY EYES

A Personal Narrative

HENRY CABOT LODGE

☆ ☆ ☆ ☆ ☆ ☆ ☆ ☆ ☆ ☆ ☆ ☆

THE STORM
HAS MANY EYES

A Personal Narrative

W · W · NORTON & COMPANY · INC · NEW YORK

B
Lodge

Copyright © 1973 by W. W. Norton & Company, Inc.

FIRST EDITION

Library of Congress Cataloging in Publication Data
Lodge, Henry Cabot, 1902–
The storm has many eyes.
I. Title.
E748.L8A37   973.9'092'4 [B]   72-10399
ISBN 0-393-07377-7

ALL RIGHTS RESERVED

Published simultaneously in Canada
by George J. McLeod Limited, Toronto
Book Designer: Robert Freese

PRINTED IN THE UNITED STATES OF AMERICA

1 2 3 4 5 6 7 8 9 0

To Emily

Contents

	Author's Note	11
	Acknowledgments	13
ONE	Early Memories	17
TWO	In the Senate	49
THREE	The Drafting of the President—1952	75
FOUR	The Cabinet and the United Nations	127
FIVE	With Khrushchev in America	157
SIX	Other Campaigns	183
SEVEN	In the Sixties	199
EIGHT	For the Future	223
	Appendix	235
	Index	265

Illustrations

Henry Cabot Lodge, Helena Lodge, John Davis Lodge, 1909.
Middlesex School Debating Team, 1920.
The author at Louisiana Maneuvers, 1941.
General Eisenhower visits the First French Army.
Colonel Lodge in Germany, 1945.
Lake Constance, Germany, April 1945.
Emily Sears Lodge with Henry Cabot Lodge.
Two Lodge brothers, 1947.
The author with General Eisenhower, Denver, Colorado,
    1952.
Campaigning in New Bedford, Massachusetts, 1952.
At the UN Security Council, 1953.
At the UN, 1953, the author with Vice-President Richard
    Nixon.
The author with V. K. Krishna Menon.
With President Dwight Eisenhower, 1954.
With Eleanor Roosevelt, 1959.
With President Harry S. Truman, 1959.

ILLUSTRATIONS

With Averell Harriman in New York City, 1957.

With Premier Nikita Khrushchev in Pittsburgh, 1959.

The author accompanies Khrushchev to the Lincoln Memorial, 1959.

Speaking in Beverly, Massachusetts, 1960.

Speaking in Florida, 1961.

A 1960 campaign photo, New York City.

In Tashkent, 1960.

In Samarkand, 1960.

A Samarkand market.

Vietnam, 1963.

Saigon, 1964.

The author sworn in as U.S. ambassador to Vietnam, 1965.

With President Johnson.

Danang, 1966.

Back from Vietnam for consultation, 1966.

The author returns to Washington to report on Vietnamese elections, 1967.

With Mrs. Dwight D. Eisenhower, New York City, 1972.

Bonn, 1968.

With Willy Brandt in Bonn, 1969.

The author and Pope Paul VI, Rome, 1971.

With President Nixon, 1971.

The illustrations appear following pages 112 and 176.

Author's Note

A man with great experience in active politics was talking recently with a friend, describing an event in which he had taken part. He talked so vividly that his friend remarked to him, "Only someone who has been at the eye of the storm could talk as you do."

But the speaker corrected him, "A meteorological storm has one eye, the center of which is calm. But man-made storms, which decide the course of human events, have many eyes— all of them turbulent. And the man who tries, in Addison's words, to 'ride the whirlwind' not only often knows failure; he frequently does not even know which eye he is in.

"Perhaps this explains the chaotic and disorderly nature of man's progress through history, described (I think, by Dr. Samuel Johnson) as resembling the journey of a drunken man on a blind horse."

And I hope it may also explain the title of this book.

H.C.L.

Acknowledgments

My thanks go
   to my wife, Emily, and to my sons, George and Harry, for
reading the manuscript and making such frank, constructive
comments;
   to Evan Thomas for his ever-professional advice and help;
   to Mrs. Beth J. Downes for repeated retypings of the manuscript;
   and to all, too numerous to mention (I have only mentioned
names where the story called for it), who worked with me
while all the events set forth in these pages were happening.
Gratefully, I see their faces around me as I write.

THE STORM HAS MANY EYES

CHAPTER ONE

☆　☆　☆　☆　☆　☆　☆　☆　☆　☆

Early Memories

My father died when I was seven. I remember him as a big, handsome man with white teeth, blue eyes, thick light-brown hair, and a deep tan. He would draw me pictures of men on stiff filing cards, making the heads out of red and blue sealing wax. He would take me to Rock Creek Park in Washington and make little sailboats out of scraps of wood, equip them with paper sails, and launch them into the creek. He rowed me around the coves of Nahant, that lean and rocky peninsula which sticks out like a pointing finger toward Europe some ten miles north of Boston. He would row me in the summer in a dory and we climbed on the rocks examining with delight the pools left at low tide.

His great interest in life was writing poetry, but he also worked in my grandfather's office in the Senate. At first we lived in a beautiful old house with a big garden at 1925 F Street which is now the "1925 F Street Club." My parents then built a house on Massachusetts Avenue, near Sheridan Circle, backing on Rock Creek Park.

Washington in those days was a sleepy Southern town. The streets were quiet. The street cars on their rails made little noise and the sound of their bells was pleasant. The clip clop of the horse-drawn taxis (known as herdics) and the almost inaudible hum of the "electrics"—the automobiles moved by storage batteries in which ladies traveled about the town— would never even drown a whisper. Gasoline autos were infrequent and the air under all the leafy archways lining the streets was clean. There were many large private houses, mostly of red-brick Federalist style, with white columns and trim, one of which was inhabited by the hospitable Wylie family whose Christmas party we attended every year. But there was also plenty of room, many vacant lots and parks—and many fewer people.

As a child I was surrounded by some remarkable people, to whom the statement of the French philosopher Montaigne applied: "It is an absolute perfection, and as it were divine, to know how, in all sincerity, to get the very most out of one's own individuality." The adults in my childhood certainly knew how to do that. Of how many can that be said today in our compressed and bureaucratic society? Has work on the production line or in great offices had a standardizing effect on human beings? Is the shrinkage of individualism the result of putting fourteen million men through the military services in World War II or of putting millions through colleges? Or was it simply because my parents knew remarkable people, who were, in Archibald MacLeish's words, the "untouched, uncoached, undoctored, untinted human self, the self itself, the man, the woman"?

My grandfather's friend from boyhood days, William Sturgis Bigelow, after becoming a doctor of medicine, left his federal house on Beacon Street in Boston to go to Japan where he lived sixteen years and became a convert to Buddhism, then a Buddhist priest, and a friend of the emperor of Japan. He was awarded the Order of the Rising Sun, and acquired the, reputedly, most beautiful and largest collections of Japanese artifacts outside of Japan (now in the Boston Museum of Fine Arts). My grandparents had two houses—one on Massachusetts Avenue in Washington and the other at East Point, Nahant, that rocky promontory sticking out into the Atlantic where I was born. The house at Nahant would be opened in June, with staff, even though my grandfather could usually not leave Washington until mid-summer. Dr. Bigelow would come from Boston and live there until late in October when the house was closed for the winter. He had a bald head, a white beard which, parted in the middle of his chin, went off in southeasterly and southwesterly directions, and a prodigious sense of humor. He was like a beloved uncle to my sister, my brother, and me.

Dr. Bigelow's house at 56 Beacon Street, with all its works of art, its high ceilings and polished floors, was our home when we were in Boston. When my father died of a heart attack on Tuckernuck Island (off Nantucket, Massachusetts) in 1909, his body was brought there, as was that of my grandfather in 1924. It was in this house that Dr. Bigelow died, having had sacred Buddhist pictures placed around his bed, when he felt death's approach. His Harvard roommate, the Episcopal bishop of Massachusetts, Bishop William Lawrence, conducted his funeral service in Boston's Trinity Church. His ashes were then sent to Japan where he received a Buddhist funeral and was buried in the Buddhist cemetery at Kyoto. In 1963 I was in Tokyo on my way to Vietnam and was visited by the Reverend Riri Nakayama, a leading Japanese Buddhist priest, who knew the whole story of William Sturgis Bigelow and gave me photographs of his grave.

Another important figure in my childhood was Henry

Adams, author of *Mont St. Michel and Chartres* and the *Education of Henry Adams*. In November 1904 (when I was two and my brother * was one) he wrote to Martha Cameron, the child of one of his closest friends, that my mother had "sent the babies in their giant baby carriage for inspection, the prettiest little show you ever saw." Both of us had long curls. He wrote again to Martha Cameron in 1905, "I want to stay in Washington and have you and St. Thomas to play with and hunt flowers in the woods. St. Thomas passed the morning with me and just went through your doll house on Wednesday." The "St. Thomas" refers to me. For some reason Henry Adams thought I looked like St. Thomas Aquinas about whom he had been writing in his book *Mont St. Michel and Chartres*. He and John Hay, the secretary of state, were close friends and had commissioned a foremost architect of the day, Henry H. Richardson, to build houses side by side on H Street, looking out over Lafayette Square at the White House. The Hay house was on the corner of Sixteenth and H, next to it was the Henry Adams house, and then the Corcoran house which went all the way to the Connecticut Avenue corner and which was inhabited by the delightful Eustis family.

Richardson was an architect of great power and originality. The insides of these two houses were, I thought, mysterious and imaginative. The Corcoran house was of an earlier epoch and had a most elegant ballroom running the length of H Street. All have been destroyed to make way for the boneyard classic style which has become so widespread in Washington. Young as I was, I felt the atmosphere created by Richardson in the Henry Adams house, but it was Martha's doll house, six feet high and big enough for a small child to move around in, which had an irresistible fascination.

* John Davis Lodge who, after serving in the Navy, became a representative in Congress, governor of Connecticut, and ambassador to Spain. He is now ambassador to Argentina.

Henry Adams had a great way with children. He invented fanciful nicknames for himself which he wanted small children to use. One of these was "Dordy." He was also very short in stature and my brother John received a maternal reprimand for once having asked him why he was so short. In an effort to make amends brother John said, at his next meeting with Henry Adams, "Dordy, I think you've grown."

Henry Adams had a younger brother, Brooks, who had married my grandmother's sister and had published a book entitled *The Degradation of the Democratic Dogma*. In the family he was considered difficult, if not impossible. Brooks Adams was a rugged individualist indeed. He had a mania for bran muffins. He also traveled a great deal, and, wherever he happened to be—and it was often in Africa or Asia—he insisted on living in a house complete with staff rather than in a hotel. My great-aunt had to start housekeeping—and try to provide bran muffins.

Theodore Roosevelt was a lifelong friend of both my grandfather's and my father's. When my father had disastrous examinations at Harvard, Theodore Roosevelt wrote him, "A dropped man is in a most unenviable position; and he is always looked down on by the very men who have encouraged him to get into that position." He wrote an introduction to my father's collected works of poetry after my father died. He said of my father in a recently discovered letter, "He was the only man I have ever met who, I feel, was a genius; I have met many men of power and talent; but he had the purple in him, he was a genius." Roosevelt gave me a bronze statue of a lion by the French sculptor, Barye, which I have to this day and which all my grandchildren admire and solicit. In what he was, did, and said he exemplified to me Aristotle's belief that a man's worth is not measured by his wealth, nor by his position in society; but by the amount of himself that he has given to his people. To him public service was an incomparable challenge. He reveled in the faith ascribed to public servants by Edmund Burke: "Those who would carry on great public schemes must be proof against the most fatiguing delays, the most mortifying disappointments, the most shocking insults, and, what is worst of all, the presumptuous judgment of the ignorant upon their design."

Edith Wharton, the novelist, was a most loyal and devoted friend to both my father and my mother. My father's death had left my mother with three small children of whom I was the oldest. In 1912 she decided to take us to Paris so that we could learn a foreign language—a decision which, although I did not like it at the time, has stood me in good stead all my life.* It was Mrs. Wharton who made all the numerous arrangements—finding an apartment, a good school, domestic help, and putting my mother in touch with all of Mrs. Wharton's many French friends.†

Mrs. Wharton lived in a magnificent eighteenth-century apartment on the rue de Varenne with a perfect staff. Later she gave this up and had two enchanting houses, one at St. Brice outside of Paris and, for the winter months, at Hyères, a most picturesque onetime medieval convent—Sainte Claire —with terraced gardens high up overlooking the Mediterranean.

* Knowing French helped in many ways: It made French courses easy in school and college; it pleased fellow Americans of French-Canadian origin in Massachusetts (and in the 1952 primary in New Hampshire) to hear French spoken, when requested; it put me into interesting duty with the French Army in World War II; it was intensely useful both at the UN where French is the official language for many members and observers, and as ambassador to Vietnam; and it makes theatergoing in Paris a delight—which grows with the years.

† I have a vivid memory of Mrs. Wharton, Walter Berry, the international lawyer, and a French friend, Henri Hubert, curator of the museum at St. Germain, meeting us at the train when we arrived in Paris and taking us through the Place de la Concorde to our hotel.

Our friendship with her, which went back to the turn of the century, continued until her death in 1938. I remember staying with her at Hyeres in January of 1924. Robert Norton, the English painter, and Gaillard Lapsley, the American-born Cambridge don, were also guests. One guest of about my age was a white Russian, William Gerhardi. He had written a novel, *Futility*, about the white Russian colony in Manchuria which I thought then, and think now, very good reading. We both stood in awe of Mrs. Wharton, as she was sometimes rather overpowering, but she liked the young and was always affectionate and most kind to me. When I left her house at Hyeres in 1924 she took me to the station and kissed me good-by!

The school which I attended in Paris from 1912 to 1914 was ahead of its time in France, with respect to physical exercise and recreation. But by American standards we were required to work very hard—all morning and all afternoon until suppertime, except for a thirty minute airing in the park. It really pressed me and taught me how to concentrate.

When the "guns of August" started firing in 1914, we were spending the summer at Dieppe on the English Channel. In our household were a much loved man—Émile, by name—who was a general handy man and a companion for my brother and me, and his sister Angèle, who cooked superlatively. I can remember the newspaper stories reporting the Austrian ultimatum to Serbia, soon to be followed by the beating of the drums in every French village, announcing that a general mobilization was under way. The streets of Dieppe were lined with farewell scenes as soldiers left—including Émile—never to return. In the village square farm horses were being assembled for use by the army, each horse with a number branded on his hoof so that he might be returned to his owner when the war was over!

23

My grandfather and grandmother were in England and anxious about us. One morning I saw a pair of tan shoes outside the door of the spare guest room which, I was told, belonged to my Uncle Gussie—Congressman Augustus P. Gardner who had married my Aunt Constance (my father's older sister). He organized automobiles and gasoline and we drove to Le Havre where we embarked on a night crossing to Southampton, England.

We had a few days there before leaving for home. On one of those days my mother took me with her to Rye, the south English town, where Henry James lived. Although born an American, he had, at the end of his life, become a naturalized Englishman because of his strong feelings about the war. We sat in a large brick-walled graden containing many mulberry trees. Standing by itself in the middle of the garden was a one-room structure—a writing room or library. Henry James seemed to me to have an elaborate style of speech, as though he were looking for the right word. Finding the conversation rather heavy I wandered around the garden eating the mulberries. We took the train back to London and the steamer to take us to the United States. A strict blackout was imposed because of German submarines. Thus ended Europe for us until the 1920s and college vacations.

On our return home came five years at Middlesex School in Concord, Massachusetts, followed by three years at Harvard College, years in which I started lifelong friendships but which did not turn out, otherwise, to be the most significant period in my life. Indeed, in the language of today's students, I did not think college was particularly "relevant" to what interested me the most, namely public affairs—politics—from every angle, not necessarily as an official participant, but as one passionately interested in such things as how to win elections, how to use the powers of government to do useful things, and how best to conduct national defense and foreign policy. Half-baked though I undoubtedly was, I thought I knew what I wanted. In spite of my views about the relevance of college, I worked hard there in order to please my grandfather.

My mother was the greatest influence in my childhood.* After her came my grandfather and my father's brother, my uncle John—an orientalist of great originality, brilliance, and charm.

In the summer at Nahant my grandfather, Doctor Bigelow, Uncle John, my brother, and I would meet, equipped with bath towels, at an inlet on the rocky shore. A flight of wooden steps, fastened to the rocks, led into deep water. Small platforms from which to dive were affixed to natural rocky shelves. The rocks were so steep that they formed a pool com-

---

* My sister Helena Lodge de Streel writes:

People have not spoken enough about our Mother's intelligence, her flashes of wit, her splendid sense of values, the passionate courage with which she met life, her tremendous love for her children and her great unselfishness. She was deeply religious. When I was about twelve, she started making books in Braille for the blind, saying that in that way she could work for others without leaving home. She kept this up more or less all her life and, as she grew too old to go out and work for charities, she reverted to it more and more and worked hard almost until the day of her death doing books in Braille for the section for the Blind at the Library of Congress. She got some touching letters. One from Helen Keller for instance. She gave us the most lovely, peaceful and happy childhood in spite of her sorrow and indeed, when I think of it and also of the relations and friends who tried to help, stimulate, protect and guide us, I feel we were blessed indeed.

My mother's house was full of order, peace and thoughtful kindness. A place where one could live and laugh and think. Everything looked lovely and smelled fresh and delicious and brought one comfort.

pletely cut off from human view. Thus we all swam in the nude—with the result that I have never since been able truly to enjoy swimming while wearing a bathing suit.

On Sundays, after the swim, we would lunch at my grandfather's house (wearing a coat and tie at my mother's direction) where we always had cold lobster, from the then unpolluted waters, with mayonnaise. This was followed by roast beef. What gastronomic orgies!

My grandfather was a grand companion and in the winter, when we were in Washington on vacation from school or college, he would take us on walks in Rock Creek Park. His house in Washington was actually two houses, combined into one. It had an enormous high-ceilinged library which we entered through a door in the west wall. To the right of the door was a fireplace six feet high which burned logs of cord length. There were two long windows facing south—onto Massachusetts Avenue. The east and north walls were completely lined with books. There was also a gallery, leading to other galleries, which we reached by a small staircase. These galleries were also lined with books. In the main gallery one could look down into the room. I remember long evenings spent in front of the fire alone with my grandfather, from 1918 until his death in 1924. He would talk to me at great length about public questions: the League of Nations, of course; but many other subjects as well, notably practical politics, local, state, and national; the functioning of the Senate, national defense, the tariff, and civil rights.

In this room family life went on. My grandfather had tremendous powers of concentration and used to sit working at his desk, sometimes with a secretary, while the rest of the family and friends had tea in front of a big Italian painting which ran from the floor to the ceiling. When some remark caught his attention, he would stop work at his desk and would

26

join us, taking out a book of essays or poetry or a volume of Shakespeare to prove his point. I remember him often standing with a book in his hand, reading some passage and obtaining our complete attention. We three children had the run of his library and I believe we all still feel that just being in a library is a happiness and a strength, although using it occasionally has its advantages too, as our grandfather never tired of pointing out. A stream of distinguished persons—congressmen, senators, journalists, diplomats, and old friends dropped in for almost every meal so that all the days were fun.

I inherited my party affiliation from my grandfather, who was the Republican leader of the Senate, and always my beloved counselor and friend. His Republicanism (he was born in 1850) stemmed from the Civil War, slavery, the Union, and Abraham Lincoln. One of the main efforts of his life was the so-called Force Bill—which provided that U.S. marshals would be sent into the South to protect the Negro in his right to vote. In becoming a Republican, I thought I was joining something affirmative, evolutionary, and idealistic—which demanded sacrifice and generosity—not a party which said no to all proposals for change.

These talks with my grandfather did not fill me with a desire to hold office. Perhaps this was because I had observed the trivial, but time-consuming, pressures on a man in public life and the way in which he is pursued by office seekers.

My grandfather, to conclude these memories of him, told me, "My boy, we do not talk about family in this country. It is enough for you to know that your grandfather is an honest man"—a remark which had been made to him by his grandfather. Nonetheless, two ancestors appealed to my boyish imagination.

One was George Cabot, my thrice great-grandfather, who, in the American Revolution, was engaged heavily in privateer-

27

ing and would have been hanged for piracy if the British had caught him.

The other was Admiral Charles Henry Davis (my grandmother's much-loved father), who, in the Civil War, commanded at the battle of Memphis (where the Confederate flotilla was destroyed) and again in the fight at Fort Pillow— for all of which he received the thanks of Congress. These battles cleared the Mississippi from Cairo, Illinois, south to Vicksburg. Admiral David G. Farragut cleared it from New Orleans north to Vicksburg, and Admiral David D. Porter attacked Vicksburg from the river while General Ulysses S. Grant was besieging it by land.

Davis gave my grandfather (who was his son-in-law) a large brass cannon which he had captured at Memphis and which stood as a newel post at the foot of the stairs in the house at Nahant. In the style of those days a kerosene lamp had been inserted into the muzzle of the cannon. It is in my home now, but has been relegated, by my wife, to the basement!

Because the Civil War was of compelling and hypnotic interest to me, I had always hankered to go to Vicksburg; so in 1972 I took a fascinating trip up the Mississippi. I remembered vaguely having heard that there was a statue of Admiral Davis in Vicksburg. At the end of a long spring day on the river, we came upon a series of high bluffs rising out of the giant Mississippi. This was Vicksburg. We disembarked and all mounted a bus to see the sights. From the top of the highest bluff the river seemed indeed a massive stream fit to drain a continent as it gleamed in the setting sun.

On top of this bluff stood a granite obelisk, about two hundred feet high. On each one of its four sides, standing at its base, were full-length bronze statutes of heroic size of the four Civil War admirals—Farragut, Porter, Davis, and A. H. Foote, who had built the riverine navy. It was stupendous.

Abraham Lincoln's utterance after Grant took Vicksburg that now "the father of waters flows unvexed to the sea" came to my mind. I remembered that my grandfather had once written to me when I was a boy, "I had rather have you like your great-grandfather Davis than anyone else." Seeing all that, so unexpectedly and in my seventieth year, sent rather youthful shivers down my spine.

But to get back, my mother had obtained a summer job for me with James T. Williams, Jr., editor of the Boston *Transcript*—slender, dark-eyed, and intense—in 1922. This work delighted me, so after college, I got a job on the *Transcript*. Three years there and six years on the New York *Herald-Tribune* provided opportunities to work in Boston, Washington, New York, and overseas, and every moment was interesting and educational.

A great character in the Boston of those days—and a perfect delight to the reporters—was Mayor James M. Curley: handsome, with a massive head, regular features, and a rich baritone voice, which could be used for savage attacks or for uttering dulcet quotations from Shakespeare.

One report (for the accuracy of every detail of which I cannot vouch) concerned his appointment of one Theodore Glynn to be the fire commissioner of Boston. This was then the greatest plum which the mayor could give, since the police commissioner of Boston was appointed by the governor of Massachusetts. Mr. Glynn was short and stocky with a bright pink complexion, bright blue eyes, and hair of a truly fiery red. What was Mayor Curley's shock a few years after appointing Commissioner Glynn to read in the paper that Glynn had decided to run against Curley when Curley came up for re-election as mayor of Boston!

The ingratitude of this action shocked the mayor and his

29

supporters. One night a testimonial dinner was given for Commissioner Glynn at the Bradford Hotel in Boston to which, of course, Mayor Curley was not invited. He nevertheless decided to attend and arrived at the door of the banquet hall accompanied by a large suite of hangers-on who applauded loudly as he made his way to the head table. Going up to the rostrum, he quickly took possession of it, gave himself a resounding introduction, and launched into his speech, the closing words of which were reported to have been somewhat as follows: "In the whole vast lexicon of the English language there is no word more despicable than that of traitor." Then came a pause. "Benedict Arnold was a traitor to George Washington. Sir Hudson Low, on the Island of St. Helena, was a traitor to Napoleon. Judas Iscariot was a traitor to our Lord Jesus Christ."

Then came an even longer pause, after which Mayor Curley said, "Funny—they all had red hair."

On July 1, 1926, in Beverly, Massachusetts, I married Emily Sears, a long-suffering young lady who says that, whatever else I may have done, I have never bored her.

I was working in the Washington bureau of the New York *Herald-Tribune* (and moonlighting as a stringer for *Time*). One morning in May of 1927 the telephone rang. I answered and a voice announced that he was "Ike" Hoover, the major-domo at the White House. President and Mrs. Coolidge, he said, would like my wife and me to come to lunch that day to meet Colonel Lindbergh and his mother. Colonel Charles A. Lindbergh had just flown the Atlantic and was arriving in Washington on a naval vessel.

I thought a colleague prone to practical jokes was indulging himself. My wife was in a frenzy of hope—and also of expectation, as our oldest son was due in a month. Finally, the voice on the telephone convinced me that it did in fact belong to

Mr. Hoover and, at the appointed hour, my wife and I walked across DuPont Circle to the temporary White House, the marble structure belonging to Mrs. "Cissie" Patterson, because the permanent White House was being repaired. An immense crowd was outside, but we were obviously expected and were ushered up a marble staircase to a drawing room where we waited until President and Mrs. Coolidge and Colonel Lindbergh and his mother came into the room. The six of us sat down to lunch, which we ate to the accompaniment of the cheers of the crowd outside. Several times Lindbergh went to the window to wave. The president, with his pale face and thin red hair, seemed in excellent humor, but conversation was sparse.

After lunch the president, Colonel Lindbergh, and I went to a small smoking room containing an office desk and a squeaky swivel chair in which the president sat, rocking to and fro as was his wont. The president put a cigar into a white celluloid holder and lit it. I smoked a cigarette. Colonel Lindbergh did neither. The silence, except for the chair squeak, was complete. Finally, the president broke the silence, "Colonel, you were in the airmail service, weren't you?"

Colonel Lindbergh replied in the affirmative.

The president asked, "Well, how did you like it? Did you find it interesting?"

Lindbergh replied, "Yes, it was quite interesting and I derived valuable experience from it. But it got rather monotonous flying over the same valleys and the same rivers and the same mountains all the time."

The president grunted and said, "Well, Colonel, just think of me out here on the *Mayflower* * year after year—same *Mayflower*, same Potomac, same banks, same everything—excepting for the changes in the seasons."

While covering the White House I met Eugene Meyer one

* *Mayflower* was the name of the presidential yacht.

day coming out after talking with President Coolidge. Meyer was a successful and charming New York financier whom Coolidge had appointed to head the Federal Farm Board and who later became the owner and publisher of the Washington *Post*. While we passed the time of day outside the West Wing of the White House, he remarked that in that year—1927— more Americans were engaged in animal husbandry than in any other single occupation; that is, in raising horses, cattle, poultry, hogs, and so forth. More than 50 percent of all Americans were engaged in agriculture. It was only a few years later that the figure of more than 50 percent of Americans engaged in farming fell to about 9 percent.

Today one of our major troubles has been that we did not foresee the disturbing sociological effects which the development of scientific agriculture would have, notably on the poorest classes of farm laborers whose jobs science destroyed and who came streaming north hoping to get work—but the big cities of the north were totally unprepared to receive them, and there was no work. It was a time of enormous change.

President Coolidge stated once that he believed in the separation of powers as provided by the Constitution and that it would no more occur to him to try to interfere with Congress or to put any kind of pressure on Congress than it would to tamper or interfere with the Supreme Court. Five years later our concept of government had reversed itself. A president who did not try to persuade and pressure Congress was considered by the public not to be doing his job—and would be so considered today.

Presidential secretaries and the organization of the presidential office have always fascinated me, bringing to mind President Coolidge's private secretary, C. Bascom Slemp, a Virginia Republican with sad bloodhound eyes. Slemp had concocted a book called *The Mind of the President*, consisting of excerpts from Coolidge's writings and sayings, arranged according to topic. Slemp told us White House journalists that this book was the answer to our prayers and that whenever we wanted to know Coolidge's view all we had to do was consult his book—and, he hoped, not bother the president with questions! What a wonderfully simple solution, unfortunately not possible even then!

Among the young lady secretaries at the White House in the Coolidge days was a personable blonde from Vermont whom I shall call Miss Brigham. Coolidge was extremely regular in his working habits. He would arrive in his oval office in the White House West Wing in the morning at five minutes before nine and almost immediately would press the buzzer, which was the signal for Miss Brigham to come in to take dictation. On one particular morning, however, one minute and then two minutes went by before the buzzer sounded. When it finally did, Miss Brigham immediately entered the presidential office and sat in the usual chair bending down over her pad, not even bothering to look to see whether the president was there or not: He was always there and everything was always the same. Moreover, she could hear him squeaking to and fro in his swivel chair.

Coolidge enjoyed rocking in his chair, bouncing the finger tips of one hand against the finger tips of the other hand and also occasionally kicking the chair around with his toes so that he could look at the Washington monument. Finally, when the pause had gone on for a minute without a word from the president, Miss Brigham looked up to see whether in truth he was there. He was there, all right, but she thought he had an odd look on his face. Finally, he stopped rocking and said, "Miss Brigham, you're a comely young person." Miss Brigham was stunned. The president then turned the chair around to look at the Washington monument and added, "You're personable, you're well-dressed, and altogether it's a pleasure to have you around."

Miss Brigham blushed to the roots of her hair and wondered what had come over the president.

Finally, after one more look at the monument, the President concluded, "I tell you this to put you in a good humor so that you may be more careful about your spelling in the future."

Coolidge was neither the first—nor the last—President to have secretarial problems. Perhaps the greatest of all stories having to do with presidential assistants was told me in the latter years of his life by Robert Lincoln O'Brien, the former chairman of the Tariff Commission, who had been a very junior aide at the White House during the administration of President Cleveland. In O'Brien's own words, as I jotted them down after hearing him,

In 1894 the correspondent of the great British News agency, Reuters, visited the White House on Saturday, November 3, to tell President Cleveland's secretary, Henry T. Thurber, of the death of Czar Alexander III of Russia and to ask for a presidential statement. It happened that President Cleveland was out of the White House on a fishing and shooting trip—pursuits which, in those days, were considered undignified for a president and which were therefore never announced in public.

Thurber, who had the exquisite manners of a very polite undertaker, not wanting to reveal the president's absence, vanished into the president's office, walked three times around the desk, came out to where the journalist was standing, his eyes wet, his hands shaking and said, "The president feels (not the president "says") that he is inexpressibly shocked and grieved by the sad event of which you have just informed him. It was not, perhaps, altogether unexpected, but it is nonetheless prostrating on that account. He thanks you for the thoughtful attention. He would make his acknowledgment in person, but cannot trust himself in this,

34

the first blush of his grief, to see or speak to anyone. But he is sensible of your beautiful behavior at this moment of affliction and he bids me assure you that—excuse the tears—you will bear the blow with Christian fortitude."

This was all duly written down and the journalist dashed back to the office and put it on the wire to Europe.

Act II of this drama occurs in the mountains of North Carolina. The reporter from the Raleigh Bureau of the Associated Press is tramping along the edge of a stream when suddenly he sees an elderly and rather corpulent man in an old raincoat and hat smoking a pipe and holding a fishing rod in his hand. Beside him is a rifle and some dead squirrels. The journalist approaches and asks if this is President Cleveland. After receiving an affirmative answer, the young reporter says, "Mr. President, I am Hawkes of the Raleigh Bureau of the Associated Press and I wanted to tell you that Czar Alexander III of Russia has just died and ask you whether you have any comment."

The President said, "Why no, I have nothing to say. I didn't know him. I don't believe in public officials making comments about all sorts of situations that they know nothing about."

All of which was dutifully written down and also put on the wire for Europe.

Act III that night was in the city room of the New York *Tribune* where the managing editor is making up the paper. Before him is the dispatch from Washington expressing the president's "prostration" and the one from Raleigh expressing his indifference. The editor puts the two side by side in parallel columns, writes this opening paragraph, "The grief of President Cleveland over the death of Czar Alexander III of Russia was seen to be diminishing tonight." Over it he put this headline: "Gradually Assuaging."

On November 7, the *Tribune* printed a scathing editorial about Secretary Henry T. Thurber, entitled "The Evolution of a Gentleman's Gentleman." Many presidential secretaries have had their troubles, but possibly none which could compare with this.

There were also tremendous individualists in the Senate during my newspaper days in Washington. No one who saw or heard him could ever forget Senator James A. Reed of Missouri. His regular features, ruddy complexion, piercing eyes, and thick white hair recalled a senator of ancient Rome, of which he was undoubtedly proud. He was always well dressed and had a capacity for ready, on-the-spot eloquence such as I have never heard equaled.

I walked into the Senate press gallery one afternoon while Senator Reed was speaking and heard him say, "Give me the radius of a man's tolerance and I will describe for you the circumference of his intelligence." Even if not exactly true in all respects, it is a neat phrase to be uttered off the cuff.

On another day, after a proposal of his had been turned down by a majority vote, he was being scornful of the majority, "Let us not talk about majority rule. The majority has been more often wrong than right. The majority crucified Christ; it cut off the ears of John Pym; it burned men at the stake; it applied the thumbscrew and the rack; its intolerance has been demonstrated through the ages." That pretty well took care of that.

He was strongly opposed to national prohibition and one day read from a book by Wayne B. Wheeler, the pallid and thin-lipped spokesman for the powerful and fanatic Anti-Saloon League. He held up the book and, looking at it, said, "I do not know what his ancestry may be, but I do know that I have gazed upon the pictures of the celebrated conspirators of the past, the countenances of those who have led in fanatical crusades, the burners of witches, the executioners who applied the torch and I saw them all again when I looked at the author of this bill." Finally, after reading a passage from the book, Senator Reed threw the book onto the floor with so much force that several pages flew out.

When there was something he did not like—which was quite often—he would describe a person or a situation as being so nauseating "as to make the gorge rise from the gizzard of an ostrich."

In the course of a debate on immigration he commented about race prejudice, "We remember that along the lines of Lexington, at Concord, at Valley Forge, at Yorktown, there stood many races of men, speaking many languages. I think there were thirty-six different languages spoken in New York before the Revolution. They had many religions. Some of them did not have any religion. They all had the religion of liberty in their hearts, the divine fires of God Almighty planted in the hearts of men, the divine fires of liberty burning there. They helped to establish and make this country. They have stood on the field of every battle that has been fought, and they have stood in the arks of peace, in the avocations of civic life, side by side with the man whose grandfather came from the same country only a little while before, and they have made good."

A great Senate wit was Senator George H. Moses of New Hampshire. In those days President Hoover was often accused by his enemies of once having applied for British citizenship; the story that he had had these feelings about Britain was in the air. Senator Moses could not resist the temptation in the middle of a speech in which the name of the president naturally occurred to say, " 'erbert 'oover." This annoyed the Republican regulars in New Hampshire and contributed to his defeat. A sense of humor, publicly displayed, is not always a political asset.

Another character in the Senate in those days was Senator Boies Penrose of Pennsylvania, one of whose bits of advice was, "never write a letter to a woman that you can't chill beer on."

The younger Senator Robert M. LaFollette, with whom I served, told me that while he was his father's secretary, he was sitting in the Senate cloakroom one afternoon, in the place where the telephones are, when Senator Penrose was called to the telephone by J. P. Morgan. According to LaFollette, Senator Penrose said, "Hello, Morgan . . . yes, yes, yes," and culminated in an explosion, "Dammit, Morgan, you run Wall Street and let me run the United States Senate!"

Penrose was chairman of the committee appointed to consider the admission of the first Mormon member, Reed Smoot of Utah. The admission of Utah to the union had caused a great furor in the country because polygamy in Utah was still legal. This excitement increased when the man elected to be the first senator from Utah turned out to be a Mormon who believed in polygamy as a doctrine. Moralistic Americans were in a tumult. The committee met and made a careful study of Reed Smoot's life. They found that, although he was a polygamist in theory, he had always been married to one wife to whom he had always been faithful and that he had led a very moral existence. This prompted Senator Penrose to say, "I would rather have a polygamist who monogs than a monogamist who polygs."

Covering Congress in those days led a newspaperman—if he was lucky—into also covering the national political conventions. In 1928 I was delighted to be told by the *Herald-Tribune* that I would have this assignment. The Republicans held their convention in Kansas City and nominated Hoover in an orderly fashion. The Democrats met in Houston, Texas, in a Saharalike heat. This was long before the days of air conditioning and the selection of Houston was attributed to the fact that the treasurer of the Democratic party was the well-known financier Jesse Jones, who later was to render many valuable services, notably as head of the Reconstruction Finance Corporation. It appeared that he had used his influence to bring the convention to his home town. It was also said that the headquarters of the various candidates were all placed in the Rice Hotel instead of being spread around through several hotels because Mr. Jones wanted it that way.

It was here that Governor Al Smith and Senator Joe Robinson of Arkansas were nominated for president and vice-president and that Franklin D. Roosevelt made his famous "Happy Warrior" speech nominating Al Smith. I was sitting on the floor about five feet from Franklin Roosevelt when he made this speech. One might forget his precise words, but one could not forget how he looked, and the magnetism he exuded.

The Rice Hotel was so crowded that it was useless for a working newspaperman to try to use the elevators. Indeed, the hotel management decided to run the elevators from the roof garden to the floor without any stops in between. There was a broad stairway leading from the lobby up to the mezzanine—a rise of about ten feet—and the crowds on the stairway were so thick that it would take twenty minutes to make that small ascension. My wandering eye happened to see Judge George W. Olvaney, the boss of Tammany Hall, go into the area behind the hotel's registration desk. At the back of this area was a door. I saw him open it and go up a flight of stairs. Evidently this was a private staircase going to the mezzanine. If it was good enough for the boss of Tammany Hall, then it was good enough for me. Tired of waiting and wet with heat, I entered the area behind the registration desk and approached the private staircase. A policeman tried to stop me. I pointed out that a man whose identity I did not know had just gone up the staircase. The policeman said with awe, "Well, that's

Judge Olvaney of Tammany Hall. He can use it, but you can't." I gave him a shove to one side and went up the stairs. This episode was exhumed in 1960—thirty-two years later and was extensively reprinted when I ran for vice-president that year.

The famous Texas character Amon G. Carter, publisher of the Ft. Worth *Star Telegram*, was in the lobby with all his Texas regalia—Stetson hat and high-heeled boots with spurs. He had introduced me to the sheriff of Ft. Worth whose gold badge was encrusted, so he told me, with real diamonds, pearls, and rubies.

Later that immensely gifted and utterly delightful man, Henry L. Mencken, invited me to sample a keg of German beer which had arrived at the port of Galveston on one of the North German Lloyd steamers. Would I come to his room on the seventeenth floor and have a glass? I accepted. I walked up to the room, as the elevators seemed to be figments of the imagination. Through the glass-enclosed shaft one could see the elevator cars flashing up and down opposite Mencken's room. But they never stopped. In the room I found Mr. Carter, the sheriff, and a reporter from the Baltimore Sun. Mr. Carter had just finished his drink and had walked out into the corridor to press the button for the elevator. No elevator stopped. Finally, after the fourth elevator had flashed by, Mr. Carter took the sheriff's pistol and fired three or four shots through the glass elevator door, turned back into the bedroom, fired two or three shots through the open window (I had dived under the bed, Mencken had gone into the closet, and the reporter from the Baltimore *Sun* had jumped into the bathroom) and then calmly took to the stairs.

The uproar was tremendous. Nobody was damaged, but Texas Rangers had swarmed into the lobby. Announcement was made on loudspeakers that no one was to leave the hotel—

the hotel at that time must have contained fifty thousand people. It was a festive Texas welcome duly appreciated by the effete Easterners.

Attending conventions with H. L. Mencken was a hilarious experience. Arriving in Chicago in 1932 a few days before the convention opened, Mencken asked me if I would like to join him in an informal investigation of how well prohibition was working in Chicago. A taxi took us to a bar which was located in a long, narrow room. Near the front door and to the left was the bar itself. Standing behind the bar was a young lady who could best be described as "gorgeous." At the end of the room was a piano and a species of male singer, in vogue at the time, known as a crooner. Mencken and I ordered drinks and, as we stood drinking, the crooner's voice became more and more objectionable. Finally, Mencken said to the young lady behind the bar, "I'd like to shoot that s.o.b." The young lady did not bat an eye or change her supercilious expression. She reached under the counter, pulled out a Thompson submachine gun, laid it on the counter and with a condescending fluttering of her eyelids said, indifferently, "Go ahead."

A hero of mine was the late General Frank R. McCoy, whom I had come to know at 1718 H Street, a unique bachelor club and rooming house where I lived before my marriage. President Theodore Roosevelt had publicly proclaimed him the finest soldier in the U.S. Army. He had been a rough rider in Cuba in 1898, right arm to Leonard Wood in Cuba and the Philippines, and commanding officer of the Fighting Sixty-ninth regiment in World War I. President Coolidge had decided to send him to Nicaragua to supervise the elections there. I went along and wrote a series of articles on the whole episode for the *Herald-Tribune*.

41

General McCoy gave me a desk at his headquarters. Sitting there, I could overhear his conversations with Nicaraguan leaders and became deeply impressed with his persuasive powers—not at all the stereotype of the military man. He could be witty or tactful or charming, as the situation required—and always intelligent and logical. Listening to him was an education which stood me in good stead throughout my life.

Another man who was not cast in any mold was Philippe Bunau-Varilla, the French engineer employed by Ferdinand de Lesseps, the builder of the Suez Canal. I was introduced to him by the famous World War I correspondent Frank H. Simonds. De Lesseps discovered that building a transisthmian canal in the American hemisphere was too much for any private company—the ground was much more difficult than at Suez and the man-killing yellow fever was an insuperable obstacle. Bunau-Varilla, in an adventure reminiscent of the Arabian nights, persuaded the United States government to abandon its preference for putting a canal through Nicaragua and to commit itself to building one at Panama, where the French company had started its work. He furnished every senator with a Nicaraguan postage stamp bearing a picture of Mt. Momotombo, a smoking volcano, to show that the Nicaraguans themselves admitted the instability of their terrain. When the northern provinces of Colombia seceded to form the Republic of Panama, Bunau-Varilla was there to write the constitution and to become the first Panamanian ambassador to Washington. He arranged with Theodore Roosevelt to have the U.S. Navy show the flag at the psychological moment.

After President Roosevelt told his cabinet of these events he asked each member to comment. When all had done so, the president turned to Philander C. Knox, the owlish attorney general, and said, "Let us now hear from the attorney general on the legal phases of the question." Knox replied, "Mr. President, if I were you, I would have no taint of legality about it."

World War I found Bunau-Varilla as Marshal Henri Philippe Pétain's chief engineering officer at Verdun where, while in his sixties, he lost his leg in combat and, under fire, perfected a system of water purification which he was later to install throughout France.

He was old when I knew him, but a great individualist whose friendship meant much to me and whom I shall always remember.

Shortly after I finished college, a regular army officer, Captain Philip Sherwood, brother of the playwright Robert Sherwood, persuaded me to join the army reserve. My interest in military matters attracted me to the yearly tours of active duty of about two weeks' duration. My first maneuvers were in 1930 in the deserts and mountains of southern New Mexico in a cavalry squadron commanded by Major Willis D. Crittenberger, who became my lifelong friend and in World War II commanded an armored division and a corps, rising to the rank of three-star general. The army in those days had the appearance of a Remington painting. Looking at soldiers then, it was easy to imagine Sheridan's ride down the valley of Virginia and Jeb Stuart's charges. We rode through the burning heat of the white sands of New Mexico. There were the cravings of thirst, the exhausted horses, and the even more exhausted reservists such as I whose legs, accustomed to the sidewalks of the East, ached from days—and nights—in the saddle. The pack trains of mules, with long ears wagging to and fro, silhouetted against the setting desert sun were unforgettable. Then at nightfall came an hour or two of sleep on the ground. The first sight at daybreak was the ears of the now rested horses on the picket line standing up straight against the first faint light of morning.

Once at the heat of noon the major and I decided to refresh ourselves at one of the rarely encountered watering troughs. As we were drinking the dirty water and sloshing it over our heads, two mules joined us, one on either side—and there were the four of us drinking together.

Another officer who later became a warm friend was Major Jacob L. Devers who was destined to become a four-star general commanding an army group in Europe—along with the only other army group commanders, Generals Omar N. Bradley (U.S.) and Bernard L. Montgomery (British). General George C. Marshall put him in charge of actually creating an armored force—in effect putting the automobile industry into the business of making tanks. General Devers's capacity to get to the heart of a matter as seen in the critiques—or analytical commentaries—which he gave at the great Louisiana manuevers in 1941, played a large part in the formation of the U.S. Army of World War II. These maneuvers ranged over the northern half of Louisiana and into East Texas and gave our generals their first chance to command large numbers of troops as they would have to do in Europe.

Major George S. Patton, the famous general of legendary bravery and dash, was also a friend—and a Massachusetts neighbor. One night as we were leaving the dinner table at his house in Washington he seized a decanter from the sideboard and, brandishing it, said to my wife, "Did you know that a decanter, if properly used, can be a lethal weapon? My grandfather killed the governor of the Bahamas with one."

Patton's originality, his love of éclat, his unguarded language—traits which annoyed some persons and delighted others—were, I always thought, deliberate and successful devices aimed at getting the attention of young soldiers.

One officer, still fuming with rage years later, told me of a visit Patton had made to his area not far from the Kasserine Pass in North Africa, in early 1943. German machine gunfire grazed the hilltop so that one had to crawl on one's stomach. Empty ration cans and unburied corpses added to the general horror. Patton's arrival had been noted by the Germans who had increased their fire, thus adding to Patton's unpopularity. As Patton started to wriggle away, he said, "Well, this isn't much of a war, but it's better than no war at all." At this my friend's rage knew no bounds and it lasted throughout his life.

I am certain, however, that Patton said this because he believed it was difficult for a man to be frightened and angry at the same time and he was afraid that the men in this exposed position were about to be overcome by fear. To avoid this he was willing to have them angry at him. He also believed that unorthodox methods can sometimes achieve surprise and win the battle faster. The faster the battle is won, the greater the soldier's chance of staying alive. But fighting it fast means going without food and sleep and is most exhausting.

There were other regular army men in addition to these three whom I came to like and admire. Devoted patriots, unselfish public servants, and keen professionals, they were an incalculable asset to the United States. Deeply critical of the way World War I had been fought, they were among those who, led by General George C. Marshall, did the thinking and planning which made victory possible in World War II. The army in those days was small and poor, but it saw clearly. When it became their all-important duty to lead young men in combat and to create the strategy for victory, they did well.

In 1932, after the conventions, I took a leave of absence from the *Herald-Tribune* to go home to Massachusetts and try my hand at some private writing. This resulted in a book, happily out of print. But it also created the opportunity for a friend,

John A. Trowt of Beverly Farms, to persuade me to run for the lower house of the Massachusetts legislature, to which I was elected in 1932. I learned how backbreaking a political campaign is.

As a member of the legislature, I was depressed by the negative attitude of certain Republicans, which not only seemed bad for the country, but was also hopelessly stupid politics. In Washington, Herbert Hoover was president. He seemed to me to be reactionary, inept in handling the depression, and ill-advised in calling out the regular army to drive the bonus marchers out of their squalid encampment. The marchers were pathetic men who, understandably, protested their misery by camping on the edge of the District of Columbia, hoping thereby to get help. Later I realized how dangerous it is to make harsh judgments, and that Mr. Hoover was an exceptional man with many talents—which he displayed as chairman of the Hoover Commission to reorganize the United States government. The times defeated him.

In the legislature the Democrats were constantly putting the no-saying Republicans into embarrassing positions. Knowing my views, Leverett Saltonstall, the speaker of the House, appointed me chairman of the House Committee on Labor and Industry. In that capacity, in May 1935, we made favorable reports on thirteen bills which had been hanging fire for years and which liberalized the Workmen's Compensation Law. They provided increased payments for a wide range of specific injuries; payment for the entire duration—even for life—to a person suffering from a total disability, such as loss of both arms or blindness; and a minimum weekly wage of $7.00—it had been heretofore as low as $.50 a week. With the help of the expert Samuel B. Horovitz, who gave his services, these bills were agreed to by representatives of labor, of industry, and the committee. Thus they all became law.

46

This so pleased organized labor that I was actually praised in a speech delivered on the floor of the House by a prominent Democrat, the late Michael J. Carroll of Lynn, one of the leading labor members, and by Representative Leo Carney of New Bedford.

This put the spotlight of public attention on me and laid the groundwork for a campaign for the United States Senate in 1936 in which I won the Republican nomination at the state convention after a hard fight and thanks to the incomparably shrewd management of Thomas W. ("Uncle Tom") White, a former collector of Internal Revenue under President Coolidge. I well remember that day: The nomination for U.S. senator was the last item on the agenda; delegates were hot and tired; my opponent, Sinclair Weeks, was strong; and there was no time to do anything more. Uncle Tom uttered this pearl of political wisdom, "Get down to the hall a little early, and stand out in the lobby and smile and shake hands as they come in. Be sure to keep smiling, because they'll think you've got it in the bag. Then just before the vote, walk across the platform slowly. Let the boys see you're there. It will make it a little harder for them to double-cross you."

Then came another hard fight—which resulted in my election to the U.S. Senate even though President Roosevelt swept the state. My opponent was James M. Curley, who was then governor. His defeat was the only instance in that year of a seat heretofore held by a Democrat going to a Republican. By then I was thirty-four years old—with a slightly exaggerated ego.

CHAPTER TWO

☆   ☆   ☆   ☆   ☆   ☆   ☆   ☆   ☆   ☆

In the Senate

The Senate of the United States is an enthralling, surprising, and great institution. I arrived there in January 1937. One of the first senators whom I met was Senator Henry Fountain Ashurst of Arizona. Tall, handsome, and with the elocution of a Shakespearean actor, his overriding trait was his uproarious sense of humor. In our first conversation, he remarked, "Senator Lodge, after you have been here a little while, you will find that you will have voted on all three sides of every question." I soon learned that there are often many more than three sides.

Senator Ashurst was chairman of the Judiciary Committee to which was referred President Roosevelt's so-called Supreme Court packing proposal—authorizing the president to appoint many new members to the Supreme Court. As a loyal Democrat Ashurst generally supported administration measures. He had, however, recently made a speech in Baltimore, before the court packing bill had been proposed, in which he had denounced any tampering with the Supreme Court. In the midst of a speech defending the court packing proposal, he was interrupted and a quotation from his Baltimore speech was read to him. He replied,

> What the senator has just read is my rhetoric; I shall not deny it.
>
> Mr. President, my faults are obvious. There can be no doubt I have my full share. I suffer from cacoethes loquendi, a mania or itch for talking, from vanity, and morbidity, and, as is obvious to everyone who knows me, an inborn, an inveterate flair for histrionics.
>
> But there never has been superadded to these vices of mine the withering, embalming vice of consistency. Whoever in his public service is handcuffed and shackled by the vice of consistency will be a man not free to act as various questions come before him from time to time; he will be a statesman locked in a prison house the keys to which are in the keeping of days and events that are dead. Let me quote Emerson: "A foolish consistency is the hobgoblin of little minds, adored by little statesmen."

This was a good introduction to the Senate of those days—with its human mixture of humor, craftiness, and patriotism.

In one sense the Senate is an excellent example of democracy—what Plato called a "charming form of government full of variety, disorder and dispensing a sort of equality to equals and unequals alike."

The Senate is not just another, smaller, House, with members apportioned among districts of approximately equal population. Its unique feature, which to some seems on occasion unjust, is that it incarnates the federal principle: the equality of large and small states alike. California and New

York each have two senators and Delaware and Rhode Island each have two senators. The one provision of the Constitution which as a practical matter cannot be amended is the provision in Article V which says, "no state, without its consent, shall be deprived of its equal suffrage in the Senate." Thus the millions in the cities often do not count as much as the thousands on the farm. And the senator from the small state, if he can just stay there long enough, can be chairman of a key committee and exert an influence out of all proportion to the number of his constituents.

Yet there is a great stability in federalism. Like a raft, "your feet are often wet, but you don't sink." Lord Acton said of it, "Federalism . . . allows of different nationalities, religions, epochs of civilization to exist in harmony side by side. It is capable of unlimited extension." It has also proven its worth for the development of large and diverse areas under one flag—such as the United States.

Winston Churchill commented that in the period after the Civil War, Congress was filled with "sad, solemn fellows. Carnegie and Rockefeller, together with Morgan in finance and Vanderbilt and Harriman in railroads, became the representative figures of the age, in striking contrast to the colorless actors upon the political scene. Though the morality of their business methods has often been questioned, these men made industrial order out of chaos. They brought the benefits of large scale production to the humblest home." * The politicians were in the background.

But then, Churchill explains, the public revolted. "From 'Pitchfork' Ben Tillman of South Carolina and 'Jerry' Simpson of Kansas (who enjoyed the nickname of 'Sockless Soc-

* See *The Great Democracies, 1815–1901*, by W. Churchill (New York: Dodd, Mead, 1956–58).

rates') to the revivalist Mary Ellen Lease, who advised the plains farmers to 'raise less corn and more Hell,' came leadership of a kind that American politics had not previously experienced." Senator George H. Moses of New Hampshire was later to call such senators "the sons of the wild jackass." Thus the Senate of the early twentieth century contained men who could not by any stretch of the imagination be called "sad, solemn fellows."

There were still a few of these individualists in the Senate when I arrived in 1937. Others, born of the Depression, were beginning to come. The leader of the tiny Republican minority was Senator Charles L. McNary of Oregon, slender, apple-cheeked, and a gentle cynic with deep insight into the realities of human aspirations. Had the Republican leaders of those days paid more attention to such realists as McNary and less attention to their own subjective notions, the party would have become competitive then.

An outstanding figure in the Senate from the start of my service there was Senator Arthur Vandenberg of Michigan. My friendship with him began when I arrived and turned into admiration as I watched his work. After the 1946 elections the Republicans organized the Senate. During the years 1947 and 1948—the whole time that Vandenberg was chairman—virtually all the important votes in the Foreign Relations Committee were unanimous—13–0. In part this reflected the mood of the country. But Vandenberg's desire to find a common ground and his extraordinary talent for doing so played a vital role. He had the high principle, the sagacity, and the talent which I thought qualified him for the presidency. His death ended these speculations.

Yet another example of the force of personal leadership was Senator Walter George of Georgia. He was that rarity—

a man whose speeches on the senate floor actually determined the fate of a bill. In a situation requiring a two-thirds vote (such as the ratification of a treaty), Senator George's opposition meant that a two-thirds vote could not be obtained, as many members only made up their minds after hearing Senator George's views.

If the composition of the Senate ever changes from individualists and toward organization men, it will be unfortunate. The Senate best serves its purpose when it contains original individualists who stimulate public thought—who not only educate and clarify, but also launch new ideas. This stimulation is perhaps the most important thing that a senator does. The voter should be quoting the latest happy phrase of his favorite senator!

Today the belief is widespread that the standing of Congress has declined; that it is the least successful of the three branches of government; that its debates are a bore and are thus hardly ever reported in the press—unlike those in the House of Commons in London where the heads of departments, being members of the House, are present on the floor; that the difficulty of getting a bill through Congress is so great as to create almost unlimited opportunities for obstructionism; and that Congress distorts the popular will twice: first, because states and gerrymandered districts are not representative slices of the U.S. and, second, because too much attention is paid to the group that yells the loudest. Finally, it is asserted that the general interest suffers because the only bills which pass are those which are backed by some highly organized minority. The communists cite this to support their contention that under our system of government the special interest is king and the general interest is forgotten and neglected. There is some truth in all this—and yet it does not tell the whole story, which is that hard and talented work in Congress can always accomplish big things.*

I had come to the Senate with four years of service in the lower house of the Massachusetts legislature by way of political experience. This was preceded by about ten years in journalism. When I was in the Massachusetts legislature the Republicans still controlled—a condition which has long since ceased. Hardly a day went by that the Republicans were not put into some embarrassing position by the tactics of the minority. Issues were constantly being raised which, in the interests of sanity, had to be voted down, but they were phrased in such a way as to make the majority look hardhearted, unimaginative, insensitive, skinflintish, and like errand boys for big business. The Democratic leadership in the Massachusetts House in those days acted on the principle of promising everything.

Washington, however, was then led by the enormous personality of President Roosevelt, who, as the Democratic governor of New York, had made a fine art out of putting the Republican legislature in Albany behind the eight-ball. He had become so clever at it that even when he arrived in Washington and found a Congress which was overwhelmingly in the hands of Democrats, he seemed to continue the old tactics of embarrassing them and keeping them off balance.

In Washington, instead of being in the majority as I had been in Boston, I was a member of the smallest assemblage of Republican senators that there had ever been. We were only

* To relieve him of a huge mass of routine detail and to help in his creative work a senator requires a staff. Otherwise he drowns. Gratefully I cite the valuable services of Chandler Bigelow, Francis McCarthy, Cammann Newberry, and Maxwell M. Rabb, close associates and warm friends.

sixteen out of ninety-six. There were not even enough of us to force a roll call vote. The committees could all function whether we were there or not. Therefore, the most important duty of the minority was to show up the inadequacies and insincerities of the party in power—particularly when they were so very large and we were so very small. This might also, with luck, help to set the Republican party on a new and more competitive course.

A study of social security provided a chance to do this: The funds accumulating under the Social Security Act had, I thought, become so great as to justify an increase in payments for old-age pensions. So, in 1939, I offered an amendment increasing old-age pension payments by one-third. This proposal was easy to understand, it attracted attention and it also had intrinsic merit. The administration was opposed to it and wanted, above all, to kill it without having a roll call. I received a bad jolt when Senator James F. Byrnes of South Carolina moved to lay my proposal on the table. This motion had the effect of cutting off all debate and of having an immediate vote. It is considered very unusual and unsenatorial. I must say that, although startled, I could not, in all candor, resent it: The majority was defending itself. When my proposal was put to a vote, I asked for a roll call and almost everybody sat on their hands. They evidently intended to kill my proposal without a roll call vote. Finally, old Senator Hiram Johnson of California arose and asked, "Is there no fairness in this body to give us the yeas and nays?" It turned out that there was—when Hiram Johnson asked for it. I had my roll call; my proposal was defeated, 39–30; and some Democrats had trouble at the polls because of it. I also learned a lesson about the vital importance of knowing the rules.

One day an administration bill appeared on the calendar to encourage the building of houses. I offered an amendment to the bill providing that all work done under its terms should be done at prevailing rates of wages. Administration leaders said that this would make the bill unworkable. Organized labor strongly favored my amendment and showered senators' offices with telegrams. President Roosevelt went so far as to say that "Senator Lodge is playing unjustifiable politics." Actually I had taken my cue from the Hoover days when it was just such "unjustifiable politics" by such masters as Senator Pat Harrison and Representative Jack Garner which had revived the Democratic party. It proved a veritable hot potato and it took months and a great deal of trouble for the administration finally to get rid of this amendment—and probably not without angering politically influential labor leaders who could injure some Democratic senators who were up for election.

Such measures, I thought, were socially good; they also helped to change and modernize the Republicans; and they revealed the contradictions within the Democratic party. They led to a *Saturday Evening Post* article by Joseph Alsop entitled "Republican with a Bite."

When Wendell Willkie ran for president in 1940, I spent many weeks on his campaign train, thinking him to be salutary for the Republican party. Willkie had been a lifelong Democrat but had become a Republican, and his nomination galled some Republican regulars. Senator "Jim" Watson of Indiana, the onetime Republican leader of the Senate, went so far as to say that he thought it was all right to "invite the fallen woman into the church, but don't make her the leader of the choir."

In the years before World War II, I was against involvement in the war and for building up the national defense. Although I would have regarded the conquest of Western Europe by Hitler as a mortal threat, I could not conceive that the Germans would take Paris and sweep over all of Europe—and how wrong I was! I did favor an immediate increase in our military strength and moved for an increase in our air force as early as May 1940. Indeed Arthur Krock of the New York *Times* reported that I had "urged compulsory military training some months before the president endorsed it"—on June 23, 1940, to be exact. Presidential endorsement came seventeen days later.

I had been re-elected to the Senate for a second term in November 1942 and I began hankering to get into the army once again as the first year of our war involvement drew to a close. My age, my extensive military training in the reserve, and my previous military service (on Louisiana and Carolina maneuvers in 1941 and with American tank crews in Libya in 1942) all convinced me that the time had come, as did the fact that the United States was then entering the period of large-scale ground fighting.

The Senate, such a fateful forum before and after the war, had, during the war, become a place without major controversy. The special committee of five senators to visit the war theaters, of which I had been a member, had made its world tour and had submitted its report. The War Department had decided to require members of Congress to choose between being either member of Congress or military men. I would have to resign if I were to perform further military service. I decided to resign.

In discussing the matter with General Marshall, the danger appeared that some politically minded individual might, after I had definitely resigned, pull strings to prevent my going overseas and station me for the duration in a dull and quiet place in the United States. General Marshall suggested that I protect myself against this possibility by telling President

Roosevelt of my intentions. He was sure that if it were known that President Roosevelt knew about my plans, no one would dare interfere. I therefore obtained an appointment to see the president.

I arrived at the White House in plenty of time and was shown into the Cabinet Room to wait. Finally, through the long French window I could see the president being wheeled at a rapid pace along the terrace by the rose garden. A cigarette in its long holder left a plume of smoke as he was wheeled up the brick ramp to his office. Admiral William D. Leahy was walking by his side.

After a short interval, I was ushered into the oval office. The president was sitting at his desk. He raised his hand, waved it at me, and said, "Hello, Cabot!" Seated in back of him and somewhat to my left was his longtime secretary and friend, Stephen Early.

The president opened with some news about the war, in particular about the fighting which had just taken place in the Pacific at Kwajalein. Then he paused with a smile and looked at me as though to say, "What's on your mind?"

"Mr. President," I said, "I have decided to resign my seat in the senate and go on combat duty in the army."

The president's eyebrows shot up and so did Early's. I shall always remember those two sets of eyebrows. Both men were obviously completely surprised.

"Cabot, that's splendid!" said the president. "I congratulate you!"

I told the president about my military training and service, that I had checked with General Willis D. Crittenberger with whom I had served in the Second Armored Division, and that General Crittenberger had a place for me as soon as I went on active duty.

"What I plan to do," I added, "if you will give me your

blessing, is to fly to England to join him before my resignation is announced in the Senate."

"Certainly you have my blessing," said the president, "I only wish I could go along with you."

Later that morning came the extraordinarily gracious and thoughtful note reproduced on page 60.

I also received this most generous and friendly letter from Senator Robert A. Taft, handwritten on his personal Washington stationery, 1688 Thirty-first Street, N.W.:

February 6, 1944

Dear Cabot—

This is just a note to say that I think you have done a very fine thing, and the right thing. I am confident you will never regret it and can always look back at it with real satisfaction. It could not have been easy to do.

I wish you the very best of luck and success in the Army. It has been a pleasure to serve with you here in Washington, and I look forward to the time when we may work together again in public life, perhaps a more constructive work than we are permitted to do in the opposition. If I can ever do anything for you here in Washington, or see anyone, don't fail to write or wire me. Don't forget us so completely as to omit asking for a ballot. Write us a letter about the war sometimes so that the Senate may have a little firsthand information. I know that all your colleagues would really appreciate it—they will follow your career with the greatest of interest and goodwill.

Sincerely
Robert Taft

I resigned in a letter which was read to the Senate on February 4, when I was on my way to England, confident that my political career was finished. In the strange workings

THE WHITE HOUSE
WASHINGTON

February 1, 1944.

<u>PERSONAL</u>

Dear Cabot:

I want you to know that I am awfully glad that you came to see me this morning. And I am writing this note to tell you that I would do just what you are doing, if I could.

I missed being with the guns in 1917-'18. It's too late now. I envy you the opportunity that is yours and I congratulate you upon the decision you have made.

Good luck, and all best wishes,

Very sincerely yours,

Franklin D. Roosevelt

Honorable Henry Cabot Lodge, Jr.,
United States Senate,
Washington, D. C.

of fate, however, I was re-elected to the Senate in 1946 by a large majority, even achieving the Republican dream of carrying the city of Boston!

Returning to the Senate after the war, I went to the bottom of the seniority list. Had I recovered my seniority, I could have displaced the ranking Republican senator, Eugene D. Milliken, on the Finance Committee or the ranking Republican senator, Alexander Wiley of Wisconsin, on the Foreign Relations Committee. I would also have been senior to Senator Taft. I asked if I could serve on the Foreign Relations Committee—something which is usually way beyond the reach of any freshman senator. As a sort of veteran's preference I was put on this committee, however, taking part in the drafting and passage of the far-reaching, novel and inventive legislation relating to aid to Greece and Turkey, the creation of the Marshall Plan, the extension of "advice" to President Truman to proceed to negotiate the North Atlantic Treaty, and the subsequent ratification of the North Atlantic Treaty. Later there came the resolution on troops to Europe.

The Senate at that time was at its best. Not only was the committee unanimous in all its important votes; there were never any leaks of official testimony. The secretary of state and other witnesses developed a feeling of confidence in our discretion. This increased our understanding and in turn increased the value of our advice and our influence.

The Truman administration was skillful in the way it presented its Marshall Plan proposal—an unprecedented undertaking to spend $14 or $15 billion. There were, of course, the presentations by General Marshall—then secretary of state—and the other members of the cabinet. They were all convincing and well expressed. The administration added a new touch—by sending particularly eloquent and clearheaded men up to Capitol Hill to carry the load of day in and day out arguments and presentation. Robert Lovett, who was then under secretary of state, and Lewis Douglas, ambassador to Great Britain, made arguments for the Marshall Plan which I still remember vividly, more than twenty-five years later. They were there not because their official positions required it, but because of their forensic talent.

In 1947 the Republicans in the Senate, so long a pitiful minority, had at last become the majority. There was thus some chance of actually getting a bill enacted into law.

Sponsoring a major bill requires much work: first, the study, consultation with experts and drafting; then hearings must be organized, witnesses produced, and individual talks held with committee members; possible amendments to satisfy critics without sacrifice of essentials must be handled with care; and great attention must be given to relations with the press and television. It is not a thing to be entered into lightly.

The proposals of real interest to me were those which got to the fundamentals of government—the basic structure which underlies everything else. I was impressed then—and still am—with the ineffectiveness of government. Very often, after legislation has been enacted, funds appropriated, and personnel appointed, nothing much happens. It was a little-known fact in 1948 that there had been no effort to organize the government in the interest of economy and efficiency since the founding of the United States in 1789. I therefore sponsored the Senate bill creating the Hoover Commission— the first effort to organize the government since the founding of the Republic. Representative Clarence Brown (Republican of Ohio) sponsored the bill in the House. The Commission made penetrating studies and far-reaching recommendations.

Following are a few examples of the follies and the waste which its studies revealed:

—A competition between the Army Engineers and the U.S. Reclamation Bureau for $50 billion of projects.

—A three-way race between the Bureaus of Soil Conservation, Reclamation, and Forest Service which had led to an interbureaucratic compromise dividing large areas of public land into checkerboard sections. One agency managed the even-numbered sections; the other, the odd numbered. All three maintained separate forestry organizations and their rangers crisscrossed each other's lands in performing their duties.

—Five to ten separate organizations of the Department of Agriculture were operating at the same time, each giving different advice on how to apply fertilizer, "thus confusing and irritating" the farmers.

—In New Orleans there were five federal hospitals, all within six miles of the center of the city, operated respectively by the Veterans' Administration, the Army, the Navy, the Navy Air Force, and the U.S. Public Health Service. Their joint capacity was 1,620 beds, but when surveyed, they had 913 patients. Unified planning later closed three of these hospitals.

—In New York City eleven major federal hospitals were found with a total capacity of 8,257 beds, but holding 5,330 patients. Four of these hospitals should have been consolidated. Yet, at the time, federal agencies were planning to build five more.

And so it went—away up into the billions.

In Washington's day there were 5 departments and 1,000 employees; in McKinley's 180 departments and 208,000 employees; and in Truman's time, when I was a senator, there were 1,812 departments with 2,100,000 employees.

The Hoover Commission produced savings of about $7 billion. It was followed by a second Hoover Commission which produced savings of over $3 billion. Of the first Commission's recommendations, 72 percent, and 64 percent of the recommendations made by the second Commission were enacted into law.

Both reports aroused strong opposition—chiefly from the well-entrenched bureaucratic fiefdoms and their allies in Congress. It was in many ways a very painful process. Yet the bill creating the Hoover Commission was enacted by a Republican Congress, signed by a Democratic president, and administered by a former Republican president.

The downfall of popular government in many parts of the world occurs when it becomes so ineffective that it can no longer translate the aims of the people into action. This must not happen here. Indeed, looking to the future, if government is to shake off its present ineffectiveness and become an efficient tool to carry out the popular will—whatever that will may be—there must be regular programs of reorganization similar in scope to those produced by the two Hoover commissions.

I feared that our electoral college system for the election of the president and vice-president could again result in the election of the candidate who received the fewest popular votes. As in today's bitter and suspicious climate, the installing of a president who has not received the most popular votes could also then have had dangerous—and possibly violent—consequences.

I therefore sponsored a constitutional amendment, first, to abolish the Electoral College. The Electoral College is the gathering (usually at the state capitol building and usually in January) of so-called presidential electors—persons chosen in the November election. (It is strange but true that the citizen does not vote directly for president, but always for these rather faceless electors.) At the Electoral College meeting these electors are supposed to vote precisely as the people have voted—but sometimes one of them will vote his own notions instead.

Having abolished this so-called college, my proposal would preserve the electoral vote and count it in proportion to the popular vote. A state's electoral vote is computed by adding the number of its congressmen (who represent population) to its two senatorial seats (which represent the equality of small and large states in the Senate—the federal principle). If you abolish a state's electoral vote and only count the popular vote, the small states would lose this two vote bonus —which is why in the past so many senators from small states have opposed a straight popular vote. Indeed I have long believed that one reason why my proposal obtained a two-thirds vote (the first time in U.S. history that such a thing had happened) is because it preserved the electoral vote, and thus the two-vote bonus which the small states enjoy. To illustrate, if you preserve the electoral vote as a counting device, as I propose, in a state having 10 electoral votes, 8 would represent the congressmen (that is, population) and 2 would represent the senators (that is, the federal principle). If the Republicans, for example, in a presidential election, received 30 percent of the popular vote, they would get 3 out of the state's 10 electoral votes and the Democrats would get 7. Under the present system the Democrats would get 10— winner take all.

My bill established the constitutional right of the people to a direct vote and it did away with the so-called unit rule—the winner-take-all system of counting electoral votes, whereby the candidate receiving a plurality of the popular vote in any given state is credited with all the electoral votes of that state regardless of how small the plurality may be.

The present electoral-college-unit-rule system is seriously defective and for the following reasons:

—The dummy office of presidential elector is in effect an inaccurate rubber stamp, since on occasion these electors actually vote against the popular will.

—The failure of a candidate to obtain a majority of electoral votes throws the election into the House of Representatives where each state has one vote. This has almost happened on a number of occasions. Had it happened in 1949, on the first ballot the result would have been: Truman 21, Dewey 20, and Thurmond 4, with 25 necessary to a choice!

—The unit-rule method of crediting all of a state's electoral votes to the candidate in each state who receives a plurality puts a tremendous premium on a few large states, limits the campaign to a minority of states, and has tended to restrict political preferment to a man who happens to live in one of a few so-called pivotal states.

—The present system has led to the election of a president who actually had a smaller popular vote than the man whom he defeated—Adams over Jackson in 1824, Hayes over Tilden in 1876, and Harrison over Cleveland in 1888.* This possibility cannot, of course, be completely eliminated without going to a straight popular election, which my proposal does not quite do as it keeps the two extra electoral votes for

* In *Ripon Forum*, May 1972, Josiah Lee Auspitz, former research director of the President's Advisory Council on Executive Organization, says in a footnote on page 7, "It seems fair to conclude that had there been direct popular election of the President in 1960, Nixon would have been declared the winner with a 50,000 vote plurality."

each state—the bonus symbolizing the federal principle of equality of large and small states in the Senate. But my proposal would much reduce the danger.

—Moreover, in pivotal states there are pressure groups which, under the present system, can sway the balance in those states. For example, in 1948 the third party candidacy of Henry A. Wallace swung all of New York's 47 votes to Dewey in spite of the fact that Truman received 45 percent of the popular vote in that state.

My proposed amendment completely preserves the rights of the small states, which, under its provisions, would retain their allocation of two electoral votes regardless of population.

It gives a more truly national character to both of our major parties and greatly enhances and invigorates the two-party system in the United States. It would neither help nor hurt either party.

This proposal passed the U.S. Senate in 1950 by a two-thirds vote—64-23. This was the first time in history that one of the houses of Congress voted by a two-thirds vote to amend our system for electing a president, even though it had been the subject of complaints since the founding of the Republic. Senator George Cabot had commented in 1789, "The defect of the Constitution in this particular instance is so obvious, and the inconvenience and absurdity of it so much felt, that I should imagine a proposition to amend it could not fail of success."

Senator Cabot was wrong; 151 years after his statement my proposal was beaten in the House by a vote of 134–210—not even receiving a simple majority, let alone the two-thirds required by the Constitution. The Republican leadership worked actively against it. A ridiculously short period of forty minutes was allowed in which to debate this matter of utterly fundamental importance. During the debate it was said that this proposal would render the Republican party impotent, deliver the Democratic party to the South, eliminate the influence of minority groups in pivotal states, encourage splinter bodies, and, finally, destroy the two-party system! Although naturally not mentioned, I suspect that one thought played a very large part: that the amendment, by encouraging the growth of a true two-party system in the South, would destroy the "rotten boroughs" of the Republican party whereby a few would-be postmasters and collectors of internal revenue had for many years picked delegates to national conventions. These "rotten boroughs" have since largely disappeared.

The historian, D. W. Brogan, called my proposal "the most ingenious" of all the many that have been made, adding, "no one is quite certain of the effect such a change would have inside some states." Evidently two-thirds of the Senate, at least, felt that the net effect of the change would be good.

Failure of subsequent attempts to reform our electoral system have been due at least in part to their not recognizing the federal principle of the equality of large and small states in the Senate. These attempts at reform would have decided the election solely in accordance with the popular vote, ignoring the bonus which comes to small states because of their two votes in the Senate. They thus did not get the support of the senators from the small states. I doubt that the senators from the small states will ever vote themselves out of this bonus which gives them influence out of proportion to their population. Future legislation, to be successful, must take this into account.

In 1949, I introduced legislation providing for the public

financing of presidential campaigns "to the exclusion of all other methods of financing." This bill sought to solve another fundamental problem—the corrupting effect of money on politics. It would have relieved presidential candidates, Republican and Democrat alike, of the necessity of rewarding individual campaign contributors and money raisers with appointments in the executive and judicial branches of the government. I believe that this pressure on all presidents, regardless of party, is unfortunate, unhealthy, and can be actually pernicious. Arthur Krock called it the "bitter yield of politics and power."

The idea of public financing of campaigns was not original with me. President Roosevelt in 1907 had recommended to Congress that basic election campaign needs be financed by the federal government as an essential cost of democratic self-government.

Will Rogers had observed that "politics has got so expensive that it takes a lot of money to get beat with."

The talk of an "office market" and of putting high executive and diplomatic missions on the auction block—all this breeding of suspicion and cynicism—would disappear overnight if the primary cause of the evil were obliterated at its roots. If there are no bidders, there can be no auction. The presidential office, because of the many important appointments which it makes, is obviously in a class by itself. Under the terms of my bill the expenses necessary to a presidential campaign, such as advertising, travel, secretarial help, television, and the like, would be paid from public funds. Some said it would cost $6 or $7 million. This seemed not too high a price to pay, if it left the president completely free to make all his major appointments on merit. Also, once the financing of presidential campaigns had been cleaned up, it

69

would be much easier to deal with campaigns for the Senate and the House of Representatives.*

In 1948 I was chairman of the Resolutions Committee at the Republican National Convention in Philadelphia—the committee which writes the party platform.

The convention adopted a platform which was, in my words at the time, "under 2,000 words long" and which contained "more than 80 separate ideas." The general tenor of the platform was that "we must do more" and that "we must think anew and act anew." It promised:

—Federal aid for housing and slum clearance where the need could not be met by private enterprise or by the states; extension and increase of federal old-age insurance; and strengthening of federal-state programs to provide more adequate hospitals, treatment of the mentally ill, and maternal and child health care.

—It favored equal opportunity to advance in life regardless of race, color, or country of origin; revision of the procedure for the election of the president which "would more accurately reflect the popular vote"; equal rights for women,

* Sig Mickelson, in *The Electric Mirror; Politics in the Age of Television* (New York: Dodd, Mead, 1972), p. 45, says, "The total cost of the 1952 election campaign, primaries and final elections, at the precinct, ward, congressional district, state and national level, ran to about $150 million. By 1964, a relatively uninteresting national election, dominated by the big victory won by Lyndon B. Johnson, cost about $200 million. By 1968 the figure had exploded to $300 million, twice the 1952 figure." Mickelson found the figure of $150 million on p. 104 of an article in the March 1970 issue of *Fortune* by Herbert E. Alexander and Harold B. Meyers and on pp. 7–8 in *The Costs of Democracy* (Chapel Hill: University of North Carolina Press, 1960), by Alexander Heard.

equality of educational opportunity for all, and the elimination of unnecessary federal bureaus.

—The foreign affairs planks said America was "deeply interested in the stability, security and liberty of other independent people" and pledged "collective security against aggression."

To say the least, this was not the usual party line.

After publishing the platform text, the "Proceedings of the National Convention" said, "When Senator Lodge completed the reading of the platform, he was greeted by vociferous and prolonged cheers." On June 28 the platform was adopted unanimously. It was widely praised in newspapers which usually did not praise Republicans.

President Truman was not slow to react. In his acceptance speech on July 14, the day of his nomination for president, he announced that he was calling the Republican Congress into special session, in effect, to enact the Republican platform—or, as he said, to halt rising prices, meet the housing crisis, provide aid to education, enact a national health program, approve civil rights legislation, raise minimum wages, increase social security benefits, finance extended power projects, revise the "present anti-Semitic, anti-Catholic displaced persons law."

The Republicans, Mr. Truman declared, said they were for all these things in their 1948 platform: "If they really meant it, all could be enacted into law in a fifteen day period . . . i.e. on the 28th day of July, which, out in Missouri, we call 'Turnip Day.' "

"The Republicans," he said, "came here three weeks ago and they wrote up a platform. I hope you all read that platform." "But the people," he added, "will not decide by listening to mere words or by reading a mere platform; they will decide on the record."

The New York *Times*'s analysis of the political situation in its July 16 issue said that the president had decided to run against the Republicans in Congress rather than to run against Dewey. He would, of course, call on Dewey to use his influence with Congress, knowing full well how slight that influence was. The Truman "strategy," said the *Times*, "is calculated to draw a distinction between Governor Thomas A. Dewey and the Republican Congress and to try to impress the country with the thesis that while Mr. Dewey's record on domestic questions may not be bad, the Republican Congressional record is." The article then reckoned that the president was taking a "great risk" because the Republicans would seize the initiative by enacting the measures where the two platforms agreed.

The Republicans took no "risk"—of that kind. The leadership in neither branch lifted a finger to enact the platform. They marked time for a few weeks and then went home. This made Mr. Truman's "strategy" for him. Mr. Truman was able to tell the country that the Republicans really didn't mean it, that they were insincere, and that they couldn't be trusted. This undoubtedly played a role in President Truman's re-election by a very narrow margin.

At the opening of Congress in January 1949, I challenged Senator Robert A. Taft for the chairmanship of the Senate Republican Policy Committee—not because I thought I could win, but because I wanted the country to see that there were Republican senators who believed that the Republican party must take a new turn and could not hope to succeed if it continued to be negative and traditional. I was defeated 28–14. My votes came mostly from the coastal states.

To illustrate what I thought the Republican line should be,

I published in 1950 an article in the *Atlantic Monthly* called "Modernize the G.O.P."; it set forth an entire Republican internal program—different from the Democrats, but which tried to be not just negative either. The article proposed tax revision designed to increase venture capital and aid small businessmen—rewarding those businesses which lowered prices, increased production, and stabilized employment. It favored a wide civil rights program, including elimination of segregation in housing and education; federal aid for hospital construction and for expensive medicines; and widened social security coverage. It stayed away from the liberal-conservative ideological strait jacket and proposed a mixture of measures which I thought were suited to the realities of human existence. It sought to build a floor below which no man would sink while putting no ceiling on how high he could rise.

There would be another chance to "modernize the GOP" in 1952.

And now, to conclude, these observations of the Senate:

In spite of a certain diffuseness which naturally occurs there, as in every political body, there is much thoroughness in the Senate's consideration of an important measure. A reading of the record of the debate on the Lend-Lease bill in 1941, for instance, will show that every aspect of the question was covered somehow or other. While a debate involving ninety-six men was naturally uneven, no important aspect was overlooked.

Also the Senate is hard to stampede—to rush. It likes to look into things, to roll the stone over and see what's underneath. It is suspicious of gaudy rhetoric.

In the long run the Senate is responsive to public opinion. There is thus very little wrong with the Senate that public

73

opinion cannot correct. If, for example, the public were to disapprove of big campaign expenses by political candidates, these expenses would stop. Today, however, nobody seems to object if a candidate plasters the state with expensively painted and brightly lighted billboards or if he buys prime time for his advertising on television. If this sort of behavior were condemned by public opinion, as I believe it is in many European countries, it would stop. With its demise would end the need to raise large sums of money—and, what is vitally important, so would the conflict between a man's obligation to his contributors and his duty to his country. I have often wondered why our journalists, of type and tube, have not looked into this with vigor: It seems to open up a veritable Pandora's box of potential news stories—and of trouble for those who ought to be troubled. And it might just fuel an indignant public demand to end the scandal of campaign contributions.

A citizen who complains about government being a tool of special interests, but who takes no interest himself in campaign expenditures, has only himself to blame. An aroused public could work miracles and thus make the government truly the servant of all the people.

CHAPTER THREE

☆ ☆ ☆ ☆ ☆ ☆ ☆ ☆ ☆ ☆

The Drafting of the President-1952

President Truman's defeat of Governor Dewey in 1948 gave the Democrats the White House for twenty years.

In 1950 the man most talked about for the Republican nomination in 1952 was Senator Robert A. Taft of Ohio, an extremely likable and honorable man, but whose views seemed to be wrong for the times. World War II was still a vivid memory and Taft had voted against arming American vessels before Pearl Harbor, selective service, the extension of selective service on the eve of Pearl Harbor, and lend-lease. These votes seemed evidence of a lack of foresight and understanding of the modern world. Also, since the end of the war, his votes against the reciprocal trade program and the North Atlantic pact gave concern to many.

If Senator Taft were nominated for president and defeated

in 1952, the Republican party would either disintegrate completely or shrink into a small minority of extreme reactionaries and, in the South, a crew of patronage-hungry professionals.* The great mass of rank and file Republican voters would desert it. This would destroy the two-party system and thus our ability to bring about orderly change in America, shaking the very foundations of our government. My estimate was that he would be defeated and that we would have a sixth Democrat presidential victory.

Many eyes began to turn to General Dwight D. Eisenhower. His magnetism, integrity, and unique experience would, it was thought, pull Americans together and raise the tone of our national life.

My personal acquaintance with General Eisenhower was meager. I had seen him a few times during the war. Once as a reservist on active duty in Louisiana in 1941 I had heard General George S. Patton say to a group of soldiers, "I will give anyone a $50 prize who will take prisoner a certain so-and-so named Colonel Eisenhower." Eisenhower was the chief of staff of the opposing army in the war games. Needless to say, Patton never had to part with his $50. Then I lunched with Eisenhower once in the Pentagon, in 1947, where the conversation was entirely about civil government.

In 1949 my conviction grew that General Eisenhower was the man to unite the country, end the Korean War, lead us

---

* A story that made the rounds of the 1948 Republican Convention was about a newspaper man who asked a Southern delegate how he felt his colleagues were going to vote. The Southern delegate reportedly scratched his head and replied, "Well, some of us is for Dewey and some of us is for Taft, and all of us is for sale." This story, though fantastic and exaggerated, reflected genuine concern. One result of the Eisenhower campaign was that it helped to start political activity throughout the South, thus bringing delegates to the convention who were more truly representative of the people.

toward full employment, and guide us in a dangerous world.

On Friday, June 9, 1950, therefore, I called on him at Columbia University (of which he was then president) and raised the possibility that a situation might very well occur in which the isolationist elements in the Republican party became so strong that the party would be on the verge of a definite turn in the wrong direction. If Senator Taft won a big victory for re-election to the Senate in Ohio that November, he would almost certainly be a strong candidate for the Republican nomination. In that event, I urged, "even though I know your great aversion to public office, I think an appeal on the grounds that it is your duty to run would give you a great deal to think about. If there is anything I can do, as a man who is in Republican politics, I would like you to call on me."

His reaction was immediate. He got up from his desk and started to walk from one corner of the room to the other. He said, "It would be the bitterest day of my life if I ever had to become involved in party politics and it would be a complete departure from everything that I have said. It would be just like a man who has been a Catholic up until the age of fifty suddenly becoming a Protestant. I cannot imagine the circumstances which would impel me to do such a thing. But I think a man who definitely has a public duty to perform and doesn't perform it is in the same category with Benedict Arnold." That was that.

In the autumn Governor Thomas E. Dewey of New York came out publicly for Eisenhower and so did I.

A year passed, with Taft's influence steadily growing. In July 1951, I asked to see General Eisenhower, whose office was by then in Paris in what used to be the Hotel Astoria on the corner of the Champs Elysées and the rue de Presbourg. He had just become NATO commander. My appointment was set for 9:00 A.M. on July 10; I had been told to stay only a very short time. I arrived at 9:00 A.M. promptly and the "very short time" lasted until 11:00 A.M. when the general asked me to lunch with him in a room adjacent to his office, to which we returned for another hour's talk after lunch.

During our discussion he said that Truman wanted to see him in Washington. This request mystified him, as he didn't know what it would involve and he was in a quandary as to what he should do.

I urged him not to go home until consideration of the Military Assistance legislation had ended, because if he came while the hearings were in progress or while it was still under consideration on the floor, he couldn't avoid a call before one of the congressional committees and this raised the possibility of his being kept away from NATO for as much as a month —at NATO's most formative time. He seemed grateful for this suggestion and later acted on it, telling Truman he had so many things to do that he couldn't come home right away. He suspected that Truman's desire to bring him home had a political undertone of some sort. He believed deeply that if he got labeled politically in any way it would destroy his usefulness as NATO commander.

At lunch we talked about political platforms. He knew that I had been chairman of the Resolutions Committee in Philadelphia in 1948 and he asked many questions on the details. He also talked about getting the progressive Southern Democrats and the progressive Northern Republicans together, and asked whether it was impossible for a senator like Lister Hill of Alabama and me both to be in the same party. He also mentioned his irritation with "big shots" who came to tell him what his duty was. He thought he could figure that out for himself.

78

At the end of our meeting I made the statement to him which I had planned to make right along and which was something as follows:

"In June of 1950, General, more than a year ago, I saw you at Columbia and said that in my opinion the neutralist and defeatist influences in the Republican party might get so strong that it would be your duty to enter politics to prevent one of our two great parties from adopting a disastrous course. I come to you today to say that the arguments which were persuasive then are a great deal more persuasive now and I urge that if you come to the conclusion that it is your duty to run for president, you let that fact leak out quietly through your political supporters, without necessarily being quoted, not later than January. Also, you must be back in the United States by March or April."

His only comment was, "I am glad I have got until January."

At the end of this meeting I felt moderately sure that he would consider it his duty to respond to a bona fide draft and I thought we would be able to get this fact known to politicians around the country some time in January; but I also realized that he would refuse to come back and campaign for the nomination. Therefore getting him nominated by the convention in opposition to so formidable an adversary as Senator Taft would involve Herculean labors.

I returned at once to Washington where Senator James H. Duff of Pennsylvania gave me the glad tidings that, while out West, he had been assured by two governors that all the governors of the nine Rocky Mountain states would be in favor of Eisenhower for president—but they do "want to know one of these days if there's going to be a ball game." He said that General Eisenhower would have to realize that the time is coming when he will "have to get across the bridge with all his troops." I then gave him a sharply focused description of my day with Eisenhower in Paris.

By September it was clear that organized progress for Eisenhower was infinitesimal. Senator Taft seemed to be making considerable headway. So I suggested that a meeting be held in the Washington office of Senator Frank Carlson of Kansas—Eisenhower's home state. At the meeting were Senator Duff and Senator Irving M. Ives of New York in addition to Senator Carlson and myself.

We agreed to look for a manager to coordinate existing efforts and to stimulate others. We set up an office in Washington under Thomas Stephens—a slender, self-effacing, ingenious, and witty man—who had worked with skill and effectiveness in the Dewey campaigns and who was secretary of the New York Republican State Committee. Mason Sears, a former Massachusetts state senator and former Republican State Committee chairman, whose powers of clear analysis were of never failing help, also worked at the office. A secretarial staff compiled mailing lists of key Republicans throughout the country. But there was no manager. By all the rules of the game the manager should be a Western man, since Eisenhower came from Kansas.

By November it had become clear that creation of some sort of national committee to win the presidential nomination for General Eisenhower was imperative. Governor Dewey arranged a meeting in New York in his suite in the Roosevelt Hotel of the men who at that time were the chief Eisenhower backers. They were:

—Herbert Brownell, who had been the campaign manager in Dewey's two successful campaigns for the nomination—with what that implied in knowledge of people and procedures. His gentle, reasonable manner and studious appearance concealed tremendous energy and a fighting spirit. He was a great planner, with an extraordinary instinct for the future, and a persuasive man of action. A man of formidable ability.

—Lucius D. Clay was a corporation executive who had been military governor of Germany. He was in command when our airlift broke the Soviet blockade of Berlin. He was gifted with the power of penetrating analysis, the courage to say what he thought, and the determination to overcome the most awesome and discouraging obstacles. He never shrank from doing something complicated and arduous, if it could contribute to winning the campaign. His lifelong friendship with General Eisenhower, added to his own good judgment, enabled him to say what would be consistent with the general's position. A career army engineer, he had a keen political sense—perhaps inherited from his father who had been a senator from Georgia. With his deep-set dark eyes, and devastating frankness he was a man to admire, to like, and to remember.

—Thomas E. Dewey, then governor of New York, had made three unsuccessful attempts to become president. The first was in 1940 when he failed to win the nomination. In 1944 and 1948 he won the nomination, but lost the election. No one had had his experience winning the Republican nomination for president. His knowledge of the procedures and people involved in the workings of conventions was vast and unrivaled. His organizing ability and drive were legendary. He had a great willingness to expend himself for a cause in which he believed. He felt keenly his responsibility as party leader to help bring about the nomination of the very best possible man in 1952. He thus wanted Eisenhower to win the Republican nomination. To the surprise of some, he was always willing to efface himself and stay in the background, because he did not want the Eisenhower movement to be hampered either by the enemies which he naturally—and inevitably—had made or by his defeats in the 1944 and 1948 elections. He anticipated that the Taft forces would try to create the impression that Eisenhower was the "Dewey candidate"—which indeed they did try to do—and he was determined to give them no justification for the charge.

—James H. Duff, the bluff, red-headed Pennsylvania senator and former governor, had an unusual instinct for public opinion and for saying the thing that the newspapers would print. In speeches he would often strike a responsive chord and utter the line which would get applause from the crowd. Before the announcement of our campaign in November 1951, when Senator Taft's managers were so active and seemed to be making so much progress, Senator Duff, virtually single-handedly, kept the Eisenhower movement alive in the public mind by going on a speaking tour and frequently saying printable things—and here and there, a few unprintable ones. Indeed he was the most outspoken man I ever knew in politics—and one of the most delightful. One day he and I were talking with a group of journalists in a corridor of the Senate Office Building when a certain senator walked by. As this senatorial colleague—let us call him Jim—disappeared around the corner, Senator Duff said to me, "Cabot, in the course of your life you may think that you will meet a stupider fellow than Jim, but you are wrong. Jim is the stupidest man you will ever meet." Of course, this was reported to Senator Jim within five minutes!

—Barak Mattingly was an adroit St. Louis lawyer, a World War I marine, a longtime member of the Republican National Committee, and a most clever and imaginative political operator and convention tactician. As the campaign advanced he recognized, as we all did, that virtually all the influential Republicans in Illinois—due largely to the influence of "Colonel" McCormick and his Chicago *Tribune*—were openly for Taft. Mattingly, therefore, persuaded a number of his friends who were leaning toward Eisenhower to announce early as delegates pledged to Taft on the first ballot, it being understood that on the second ballot they would leave Taft and vote for Eisenhower. Actually, there never was a second ballot—which I sometimes regretted, as it would have been a treat to see the "Colonel's" face when nineteen of "his" delegates voted for Eisenhower. Mattingly had a slow smile, a pleasant manner, and extraordinary ingenuity.

The struggle to get a manager now began. Dewey had suggested Mattingly. Duff, who had arrived late, objected to Mattingly because he was not "well enough known." Duff told me later that he liked Mattingly personally, became very friendly with him, and that Mattingly never bore him a grudge. Harry Darby, the former national committeeman and senator from Kansas, sent word that he objected to Mattingly. Other names were suggested, to all of which objections were made. Suggestions of Western names were usually blocked by the Westerners present.

Suddenly Duff stood up and, pointing his finger at me, said, "Cabot Lodge is the man to be campaign manager and he is the only man with whom you can win." Late in the evening I was asked to be the manager. This surprised me, as I had never thought of myself in this role; but I said that if I was the man most agreeable to all elements, then I would consider it very seriously. I had been so discouraged by the differences existing between the several factions in the Eisenhower movement and the extreme difficulty of getting someone on whom they could all agree that I felt I had to accept —knowing it would create complications in my own campaign for re-election to the senate that same year.

I had also become convinced that Eisenhower possessed

qualifications for the presidency which are rarely found and were sorely needed: knowledge of international relations, military affairs, and of government generally, and a deep faith in our institutions—in the purpose of America as stated in the Declaration of Independence and in the Preamble to the Constitution. He knew that the struggle to assure the "inalienable rights" of "all men" had not yet been won and that the continued existence of poverty and of the ghettos showed that the admonition of the Constitution to "establish justice" had not been fulfilled. I was sure that he believed that the purposes were noble and should be carried out. I was also impressed with Eisenhower's intuition, instinct, and magnetism. He had great consideration for others. He had accomplishments to his credit which in some ways were more complex than most problems faced in the presidency. He was entirely free from the usual nagging ambition. His stature was quite unequaled. He would be one Republican who, if nominated, would surely be elected, thus saving the two party system which then, after twenty years of Democratic incumbency, staggered on the edge of abyss.

So I became the campaign manager—not that my talents were spectacular, but my political background enabled me to bridge the gaps between factions and thus be the man on whom all could agree. I was not a longtime Dewey man. I had supported Willkie in 1940 and in 1948 I had tried to arrange a deadlock between Taft and Dewey so that Senator Vandenberg might be nominated.

General Eisenhower's approval for this decision was not formally sought because we did not want to embarrass him in the midst of his duties as NATO commander and we did not want to put him in the position of being in any way responsible for the campaign to draft him into the presidency. He was, of course, kept informed and there was never any doubt that he believed that the campaign, which we were all running, was in good hands. So, on we marched.

A public announcement was made November 16, 1951, and two rooms were hired at the Commodore Hotel in New York, staffed by Geraldine Creagan, former secretary to Senator Vandenberg, Thomas Stephens, Maxwell M. Rabb, my former Senate assistant and loyal friend, and Mason Sears.

In the convenient language sometimes used at the Vatican, I was the campaign manager in a "collegial" sense and tried to take full advantage of the brains, experience, and drive of my associates, each of whom did a lot of managing on his own. The purpose of having one publicly announced manager was to insure that the Eisenhower movement spoke with one voice and acted in a coordinated way. As the campaign progressed, the occasions when it was symbolically necessary to have the manager physically present multiplied and by June it seemed that I spent more time in the air than on the ground, an exciting state of affairs, but my long legs had often to cope with beds which were too short and seats which were too close together.

For the nine months following November 16 I accepted every invitation on TV and radio, never turned down a press conference, and never slept more than three nights in a row in the same bed. Hotels, banquet food, airports, telephones, journalists, and politicians—such was the life of a man who, in Norman Mailer's graphic phrase, was trying to put his "hand on the rump of history."

November and December 1951 were difficult months: We did not know what Eisenhower was going to say or do, we lacked money, and help was slow to come in. We had not fully realized, with all its implications, that the general would not return until a few short weeks before the convention and that army regulations would prevent his making any kind of politically helpful statement while he was abroad. We had not really faced up to the fact that, in every sense of the word, we would have to organize a draft.

It was this stark and unprecedented prospect which was to make the 1952 contest so different from the usual political "horse race."

In November of 1951, we received our first financial help for such bare essentials as telephones and plane tickets, primarily from the Manhattan Committee for Better Government—a committee formed by my intelligent, determined, and hard-to-resist brother-in-law, Henry Sears. As we moved ahead we needed ever-larger amounts; therefore, an Eisenhower Finance Committee was established thanks to the tremendously effective backing and enthusiasm of John H. Whitney, a tower of strength from beginning to end. Howard Peterson of Philadelphia was chairman. Henry Sears and his organization worked with them. Harold Talbott, Dewey's money raiser, also raised substantial amounts.

Every week or so we would meet—usually at the Commodore in New York. Our meetings were secret and the press never learned of them. Indeed our names were not announced until we all lunched with Eisenhower at the Faculty Club at Columbia when he returned in June. In this way we hoped to mystify our opponents. Also we did not want the many Ike supporters throughout the country to feel that they were being left out. So we took the colorless title of Initial Advisory Group.*

* The names of the members of the Initial Advisory Group were thus only published once—in the New York *Times* for June 8, 1952, in its report of the lunch at the Columbia Faculty Club on June 7, as follows: "Those who sat in on the luncheon conference were Governor Dewey, Senator Henry Cabot Lodge of Massachusetts, Senator James H. Duff of Pennsylvania, Lieut. Gen. Lucius D. Clay, retired;

Many talented individuals helped: In December, Sigurd Larmon, head of Young & Rubicam, the advertising agency, gave us his services. He worked without cease to help the state Ike organizations with billboards, newspaper ads, radio and television time. Earl Newsom, the public relations man with a statesman's insight, advised against succumbing to the temptation of tactics which were tricky or contrived. Gabriel Hauge, now a leading New York banker, was in charge of research.

During this early period we telephoned day and night to every state in the union to set up Eisenhower organizations. Many state organizations were started this way, and it was not until Chicago that I personally saw many of our hardest workers with whom I had talked at length by telephone— not a bad system as it gave them more latitude and responsibility.

In early December, Guy Gabrielson, chairman of the Republican National Committee, telephoned that there was to be a meeting in San Francisco on January 18 of the members of the Republican National Committee and of the Republican leaders from the ten Western states—professional politicians all. The presidential candidates were to be invited too. It was being organized as a miniature convention. He sent me a letter to transmit to General Eisenhower inviting him to come.

Not being then intimately familiar with all facets of the general's position regarding a campaign for the presidency, I

Herbert Brownell, Jr., former Republican National chairman, Barak T. Mattingly, former National Committeeman from Missouri; Arthur H. Vandenberg, Jr., the general's political secretary; Thomas E. Stephens, secretary of the New York State Republican Committee, and J. Russel Sprague, National Committeeman for New York." The following members of the group were absent: Paul G. Hoffman, former Senator Harry Darby of Kansas, and Senator Frank Carlson of Kansas.

wrote to him on December 3, giving him Gabrielson's invitation and saying, "I can't emphasize too strongly my hope that you will be able to attend this meeting," adding that it would be "impossible" to wait until spring. Political leaders, I said, "cannot understand why . . . you do not get out into the open." I closed with the statement that "all of the men on whom I depend for political advice" agreed. Here was the reply:

D D E

Supreme Headquarters
Allied Powers Europe
12 December 1951

PERSONAL AND CONFIDENTIAL

Dear Cabot:

Your letter of the 3rd reached me just a few days ago. I am grateful for such a forthright exposition of your views and have considered the whole matter at some length before attempting to reply. In this letter, I give you certain conclusions reached as a result of your presentations. Of course, I mean to be friendly and sympathetic but, in view of the revolutionary change you state to be necessary in my attitude and actions, I must be completely frank, particularly in emphasizing again the limitations that propriety, ethics, and custom impose upon me.

The reason that a very frank and full analysis of the situation is now necessary is the change brought about by your emphatic conclusion that mere assurance that I would not repudiate the efforts of my friends is no longer sufficient.

I accept, without reservation, your observations and comments on the political scene at home; you fully convince me of the impracticability of nominating an individual who, for any reason, must remain inactive in the political field prior to the National Conventions. From my viewpoint, this is an entirely new factor in the problem; and, since my current responsibilities make pre-convention activity impossible for me, the program in which you and your close political associates are now engaged should, logically, be abandoned. To this, I assume you agree. Under no circumstances should friends, whom I admire and respect, continue to work on a project involving me when they have become convinced that my personal convictions condemn their efforts, in advance, to futility and defeat.

There is nothing revolutionary or radical in what I am now saying. I have always insisted over the past few years that it would be difficult for me to envision circumstances that could possibly draw me into a pre-convention role. Since the day of my assignment to the critical military post I now occupy, this instinctive conclusion has, for me at least, been transformed into obvious and incontrovertible fact.

Most of those who have urged me to enter the political world have agreed as to the importance of preventing a Communistic domination of Europe. They have also expressed agreement with the conclusion that partisan activity by the American Commander of NATO would dangerously divide American support of the job of producing collective security for the free world. Therefore, they have engaged themselves in an undertaking to place before me a summons to duty as their standard bearer, a duty which would, by common consent in our country, take priority over the one I am now performing.

With these things understood, I have, out of regard for the opinions of people I respect, agreed to one thing and to one thing only; namely, to avoid repudiation of the efforts of these friends and their associates. Never have I agreed to any personal pre-convention activity of a political nature. But there is a vast difference between responding to a duty imposed by a National Convention and the seeking of a nomination.

I realize that you and your group may feel that some explanation is due the public to account for abandonment of your current effort. This, I suppose, would require a recitation of the essentials of the current situation; namely, that (a) your group has come to the conclusion that the nomination of any individual without his active participation is an impossibility, and (b) since this kind of action is impossible for me in my position as a military commander in NATO, there is no other course open to your group.

If there is anything in this letter that is contrary to your understanding of the situation as it has existed and has now developed, I regret it most sincerely.

I could not close such a letter without expressing to you and, through you, to all of those who have been associated with you, the very great sense of pride I have in the knowledge that such a distinguished group of Americans should consider me worthy of occupying what is, of course, the greatest position an American citizen could possibly achieve. In fact, it was the character of the men who urged me to do so that caused me to give any consideration whatsoever to possible political responsibilities; I have never had any personal aspirations to such office. As you know, my personal inclination has been the reverse. So far as my abilities allow, I hope to continue to serve our country as long as I live. But realization of such a hope certainly does not require occupation of a political office.

My warm greetings to you and your associates. I hope that you will convey to each of them, not only an expression of the convictions I have tried to outline, but also my gratitude and cordial good wishes.

With personal regard,

Sincerely,
Dwight D. Eisenhower

PERSONAL AND CONFIDENTIAL

This made it very clear he would agree to one thing only: "namely, to avoid repudiation" of our efforts. He would not campaign. He would not seek the nomination. He would not change his plans. He would simply and solely not "repudiate." Discouraging as this was, and incomprehensible to politicians all over America, it did at least have a clarifying effect on me.

I answered immediately, writing that I was glad that the general would not oppose our efforts, "which have assumed great proportions, to obtain the Republican nomination for you." I added that "I am confident of success. The progress already made has been most encouraging. We are continuing, full steam ahead, to win the nomination."

The general's answer appears on the next page:

Still overflowing with wishful thinking, I had drawn the conclusion from a conversation with General Clay in December that there was a chance that General Eisenhower might come back for an occasional appearance. I soon realized that General Clay had neither said nor implied any such thing and that the error had been wholly mine. In explanation I cite my eagerness to win the nomination for General Eisenhower, but also my ignorance of the many factors governing General Eisenhower's position—factors which were, of course, known in all their detailed complexity to General Clay. These became crystal clear to me later, but in December I was a campaign manager, clutching at straws, and thinking only as a politician.

Since Eisenhower would not come home, the Ike Committee sent me to San Francisco. Senator Taft then sent one of his managers, David Ingalls—a personable man—in his place.

Believing this to be the biggest and most important Republican gathering before the convention, we decided to make a trial run out of it for the Eisenhower staff—a maneu-

☆☆
☆☆

DDE

Supreme Headquarters
Allied Powers Europe
29 December 1951

PERSONAL AND CONFIDENTIAL

Dear Cabot:

Thank you very much for your note of December 22nd which assures me that you clearly understand the position I shall maintain with respect to the effort you and your friends are making. It should be quite clear - at least in my view - that I have no right whatsoever to say or do anything that could possibly tend to divide along partisan lines American thinking toward the job of producing collective security. Consequently, I shall abstain from any action or word of this kind as long as I am on this job.

It is entirely possible that I may have inadvertently given General Clay a contrary impression from that which I expressed to you. I know one thing: my confidence in General Clay is such, his accuracy in interpretation is so great, and his personal loyalty to me is so complete, that nothing he could ever say about me could be contrary to his belief as to what I would want him to say. If an error was made, therefore, it was mine, and I assure you that Clay retains my complete confidence and friendship. This I cannot overstate.

Sincerely,

Eisenhower

The Honorable Henry Cabot Lodge, Jr.
United States Senator
Beverly, Massachusetts

ver in convention tactics. Some twenty Eisenhower workers went to San Francisco two days ahead of time, determined to "surround" the whole thing.

In order to start the meeting off with a bang, we arranged for a poll to be taken of Senator Taft's home town of Cincinnati, Ohio. It showed that four out of five people who voted for him for senator in 1950 would in a presidential contest vote for Ike in 1952. This poll was widely distributed at San Francisco. We hired school children to put copies under the door of everyone attending the meeting.

David Ingalls began the proceedings by describing Eisenhower as a "glamour boy." "We don't want to turn the party over to a good-looking mortician," he said. Our argument was that Eisenhower would attract the Democrats and Independents without whom we could not win. At the end of the first day of speech making, we never quite knew why, the sense of the meeting turned from one hostile to Eisenhower to one friendly to him. When the Ike men first arrived, the delegates left us strictly alone in our rooms in the Fairmont Hotel. Later, after the speeches, many key Republicans came to talk and were willing to be seen with us. The upshot of the mock convention was that the politicians who control many delegates recognized for the first time that the Eisenhower men were gritting their teeth and that a professional organization was in the making.

From the beginning our thoughts kept turning to the New Hampshire primary in March. Senator Taft was publicly asking, Why doesn't Eisenhower campaign? Why doesn't he tell us where he stands? What does he think of this or that? Is he a Republican? Will he run? According to the copy of a letter which was sent to me, Senator Owen Brewster of Maine had written to a friend:

> I returned from Europe pretty well convinced that Eisenhower will not be a candidate because: 1. his health will not permit; 2. his job will not permit; 3. his political perspicacity will not permit.
>
> Twelve European countries are hanging around his neck with all the Ambassadors, Generals, and politicians and in addition there are all the visiting firemen from over here pouring in on him each week-end.
>
> The man is giving everything he has to the job in trying to mobilize Europe and one knows how impossible that is with everyone dragging their feet.
>
> He goes at it with fervor but will not be able to extricate himself for a long time to come as Truman knows very well.

This kind of talk persuaded us that something big and positive had to be done. In early December we decided, therefore, that I would write Governor Sherman Adams of New Hampshire asking that Eisenhower's name be put on the ballot for the New Hampshire primary.

William A. Robinson, publisher of the New York *Herald-Tribune* and a close friend of the Eisenhowers, flew to Europe to spend Christmas Day with them. He was due back the day after Christmas. I went to New York and waited for him at the Commodore. His plane was late (and my impatience was hard to control), but finally he arrived, bringing his message: The general would not repudiate our action in entering him in the Republican primary in New Hampshire; the army regulations made it impossible for him to undertake political activity of any kind; he would be willing to return in June, but would do nothing before that time;

and after that he would not lift a finger to get the nomination. Duff and others had been so insistent that he must come back at once and that he must actively campaign for the nomination that this message seemed very inadequate to me. However, there it was.

We announced a press conference a week ahead of time for Sunday morning, January 6, in Washington. We argued heatedly about the choice of Sunday. The whole business seemed too risky. To require the press to arise early on a Sunday morning would annoy them. If the conference should flop, it would be disastrous. I favored Sunday because if we hit the Monday morning papers, which are usually "empty," we would get maximum publicity. And we needed publicity badly to keep the Eisenhower movement alive, so that politicians throughout the country would at least not become committed to Taft.

The press conference was held on January 6 at the Shoreham Hotel and I read the letter I was sending to Governor Adams in reply to the pro forma letter he had sent to all contenders concerning New Hampshire law. My letter said:

January 4, 1952

Hon. Sherman Adams
Governor of New Hampshire
Concord, New Hampshire:

I have your letter concerning the New Hampshire law governing the conduct of your primaries for the Presidential nomination.

As I understand it, members of both parties will be asked to sign petitions for General Eisenhower's candidacy, at the time swearing that the general is a member of the same political party as the signer.

I cannot refer this matter to General Eisenhower because, as a member of the Army on active duty, he is prohibited by Army regulations from engaging directly or indirectly in a nomination campaign. Army regulations No. 600-10 reads in part as follows:

> **** the prohibition includes *** participation in political campaign *** or any other public activity looking to the influencing of an election or the solicitation of votes for themselves or others.

In the circumstances, therefore, I consider it incumbent on me to divulge certain conversations which I had with General Eisenhower while he was serving in a civilian capacity at Columbia University.

Senator Duff and Senator Carlson and others have told me that they have had similar conversations. During these discussions he specifically said that his voting record was that of a Republican. He also pointed out that his political convictions coincided with enlightened Republican doctrine and that the family tradition was Republican.

In these circumstances, the signers of the Republican petition are completely secure in their signed sworn statement that General Eisenhower is a member of their party. On the other hand, the Democratic petitioners are swearing to something that is contrary to fact.

It is worth noting that in our conversations with General Eisenhower he pointed out that he would never seek public office but would consider a call to political service by the will of the party and the people to be the highest form of duty.

I therefore authorize you to enter the name of Dwight Eisenhower in the primary election for the expression of the preference of the Republicans of the State of New Hampshire for President of the United States.

Our simple task is to see that the will of the people, as expressed in all the polls from coast to coast, is asserted at the convention, as it will be at the election. Failure to secure a true expression of public opinion would constitute a mockery of our free system in this citadel of freedom.

Very sincerely yours,
Henry Cabot Lodge, Jr.

Journalists asked what Eisenhower would say to all this: Would he run? Was he a Republican? I replied, "Ask him and see," saying that either Eisenhower would confirm the report or he would repudiate his campaign manager and that they'd have news either way. They got Paris on the phone that night. A colonel answered and said he knew nothing of the matter. After a day's delay Eisenhower issued a statement of support of what had been done; the race was on. Following is Eisenhower's statement of January 7:

Senator Lodge's announcement of yesterday as reported in the press gives an accurate account of the general tenor of my political convictions and of my Republican voting record. He was correct also in stating that I would not seek nomination to political office.

I have frequently and publicly expressed my refusal to do so.

My convictions in this regard have been reinforced by the character and importance of the duty with which I was charged more than a year ago by our country and the other nations of the North Atlantic Treaty Organization. America's enlightened self-interest and the future of Western civilization alike demand success in our collective effort to produce security against communistic threat and to preserve peace.

Under no circumstances will I ask for relief from assignment in order to seek nomination to political office and I shall not participate in the pre-convention activities of others who may have such an intention with respect to me.

97

Of course there is no question of the right of American citizens to organize in pursuit of their common convictions. I realize that Senator Lodge and his associates are exercising this right in an attempt to place before me next July a duty would transcend my present responsibility. In the absence, however, of a clear-cut call to political duty I shall continue to devote my full attention and energies to the performance of the vital task to which I am assigned.

This established these facts: He was a Republican, he would be a candidate in the New Hampshire primaries, and he would accept the nomination if he received it. But he also made it clear that he could not campaign while in uniform, would not ask to be relieved from his NATO assignment, and would not participate personally, at firsthand, in any preconvention activities.

His conviction that one should not campaign for the presidency seemed unaffected by the fact that most of our ablest presidents had actively sought the office. In 1959, C. L. Sulzberger, reporting an interview with Eisenhower, said that Eisenhower believed "automatically that any man who wanted to be a candidate for the presidency was not qualified for the job. No man of any sense would aspire to the job; it had to be thrust upon him. He was inclined to oppose anyone who sought the job. He remembered how long it had taken when people worked on him to persuade him to accept the Republican nomination." *

The news coverage given to the letter to Governor Adams surpassed all our expectations. It dominated the front pages for three days. Even Prime Minister Churchill, who was in Washington at the time, was relegated to the inside pages.

In February we authorized Tex McCrary, a New York

* C. L. Sulzberger, *The Last of the Giants* (New York: Macmillan, 1970), p. 578.

radio and TV man, to hold an Ike rally at Madison Square Garden in New York. Some New York theater critics said, with some justice, that it was a very mediocre effort. (One feature consisted of McCrary's attractive wife—Jinx Falkenburg—batting tennis balls at the audience.) But that was not our point. We thought that to bring thirty thousand people to a hall nine months before election day at 11:00 P.M. on a cold February night for the kind of meeting usually held just before election would be extremely impressive to political minded people. And it was. Politicians throughout the country had been impressed. Also, Eisenhower had watched films of the meeting, which had been flown to Paris that very same night by Jacqueline Cochrane, and had been surprised by the size of the crowd and their apparent interest.

A few weeks later, on the eve of the New Hampshire primaries, the Eisenhower movement went into its worst tailspin. Earlier some Eisenhower supporters in New Hampshire had said that their state was "in the bag for Ike." This was a mistake. It meant that we had to win every single contest just to live up to this thoughtless boast; whereas, if we lost even one delegate, it would be a victory for Taft. Following this boast, Taft decided to enter New Hampshire and campaign in person. It became painfully evident that if the contest was even halfway lost to Taft, it would be a very serious blow to our campaign. And we were getting reports of growing Taft sentiment in New Hampshire. Also, Harold Stassen had entered the race and every vote he got would cost us an Eisenhower vote.

At this crucial time the Ike organization started to run out of money. It became harder and harder to get workers. However, we decided to sink every penny into the New Hampshire primary and sent Tom Stephens there for a month to help the organization being built by Governor Adams. Sig

Larmon also went to work on advertising. Sample ballots were printed for each of the more than 250 precincts in the state. Each had to be printed differently because the order of delegates changed with each precinct. The sample ballot was marked to show where to put a vote for Eisenhower and was handed to every single voter. It was grueling—but most effective.

Eisenhower won both the preferential vote and all fourteen delegates. Three of the lesser-known delegates were pulled through almost entirely because the sample ballot made it clear to Eisenhower supporters how they should mark their ballots. The money to pay for this sample ballot was raised by General Clay—in Texas.

Soon after the New Hampshire primary I received the following letter:

D D E

Supreme Headquarters
Allied Powers Europe
18 March 1952

Dear Senator Lodge:
For some time I have been meaning to write you a letter to express my admiration for the way you seem to find time, in spite of all your other preoccupations, to carry the great leadership burdens you have voluntarily picked up in the Republican Party's current political struggles. It is remarkable to me that you can continue to do this job so well and still devote major attention to your Senatorial duties as, of course, you are compelled to do. I now understand from General Clay that you are planning to make certain additions to your organization so as to reduce the size of your regular overload. When he mentioned to me the personalities you have in mind, I must say I was delighted.

It is a great comfort to me to have General Clay so willing to serve as liaison between me and your group. When he gives me advice, he takes off the gloves and pounds pretty hard, but my friendship for him is so deep that I still enjoy it.

As you and your associates study the results from New Hampshire, I know that you must feel highly gratified that the first visible results of your long and hard work are beginning to show up. To everyone who has sent me a congratulatory message on the New Hampshire Primary, I have replied to the effect that the credit belongs to a vast group of loyal Americans. Among those I have mentioned is, firstly, the group comprising the National Committee. To this I have added Governor Adams and his distinguished group of State Delegates; your loyal supporters throughout the nation; and, of course, not forgetting the Republican voters of New Hampshire.

I keenly realize that I am of no direct help in all the matters of policy and decision with which you are continuously faced. But I feel, on the other hand, that as long as I am performing a national duty and doing it as well as I know how, I am possibly providing as much ammunition for your guns as I could in any other way.

Possibly you have read my public expression of pride in the New Hampshire result. I think it is clear that, no matter how humbly any American might regard his own potentialities as a political leader, he could not help also feeling very set up.

I scarcely need to assure you again of the great sense of distinction I feel in your assumption of leadership of this effort.

With warm personal regard and continuing best wishes,

As ever,

Dwight D. Eisenhower

The New Hampshire primary marked the first big turning point in the Eisenhower campaign. After the victory we made a determined effort to get more full-time help, believing that it was impossible to continue on a shoestring basis. The effort succeeded: Herbert Brownell joined us full time. Then Paul Hoffman, the onetime administrator of the Marshall Plan, became active. His persuasiveness, his sense of the needs of the journalists, and his knowledge of people who could help were most productive. More money came in and Walter Williams of Washington state agreed to head the Citizens Committee for Eisenhower—the hue-and-cry organization where enthusiasts could work to their heart's content.

We won a number of other primaries, the one in Minnesota being especially impressive as it was a write-in of Eisenhower's name.

I made countless speaking tours—the job of the front man —while Brownell ran our headquarters. He also did all the talking that was done with Governor John S. Fine of Pennsylvania, who was not committing himself. Brownell, Clay, and I at various times talked with Arthur Summerfield, of Michigan, who was also noncommittal. And Brownell went to Texas—a trip which had far-reaching consequences, as will appear.

The Taft campaign obviously depended on the professional Republican delegates from the South, and the Middle Western bloc. Ohio, Indiana, and Illinois, being sure for Taft, we concentrated on Michigan, Iowa, and Missouri, which we hoped were still uncommitted. When I had spoken to Summerfield in November, he had been noncommittal, but at least had not come out for Taft, although such a close personal friend of his as the effective and perspicacious Thomas

E. Coleman (and one of the ablest of Taft managers) was pressing him. Coleman was the Republican leader of Wisconsin. He worked at politics all year round, had strong convictions, a clear head, a capacity to see the essentials, and a great deal of drive.

In April I went to Texas where former Governor William P. Hobby told me to expect some "rough stuff" at the forthcoming Republican state convention at Mineral Wells. He said that Eisenhower had cleanly won the primary election for delegates but that the Taft people did not intend to accept his victory.

On April 4 I flew to Paris to see Eisenhower—for the first time since the campaign had started in November 1951. The press at the airport and at the hotel appeared enthusiastic. The next morning I called on Eisenhower at his corner office on the ground floor of NATO headquarters at Roquencourt, outside of Paris. He was seated before a table bearing the flags of the NATO countries.

My briefing on what had happened thus far in the campaign and on what was coming up was followed by an outline of what Senator Taft's tactics were likely to be—exaggerated claims of delegate strength and attempts to portray Eisenhower as the tool of Dewey.

While lunching at NATO's officer's mess on trout caught by Eisenhower in the pool in front of his house, officers on the general's staff from Europe and the United States asked me about the American political situation. The Eisenhower political movement dominated the conversation.

At supper at the Eisenhowers' house, I told Mrs. Eisenhower that my prescription as campaign manager was that the candidate should always get enough sleep to assure a "fresh and enthusiastic" mien. He must keep his "sparkle." Eisenhower should always be "in character"—his true self, not a personage created by "political experts."

Tension and excitement mounted as the convention neared. Evidently I wrote the general on May 16 (I cannot find my letter) suggesting a course for him to follow which was intended to be politically advantageous. In reply came this letter:

D D E

At The Hague
20 May 1952

Dear Senator Lodge:
Thank you very much for your letter of the 16th. I recognize the force of what you have to say. Yet I am compelled to remark that I believe what I believe. It has never occurred to me to wonder whether my convictions can be interpreted as pertaining to the right or to the left. In fact, these terms annoy me. A man goes right or left from where he is standing at any given moment. And I think that even in politics when we try to use them in the absolute sense, we frequently confuse ourselves.

At one time, a man was of the left because he was of the Jeffersonian school and believed that the least government was the best government. Now, according to some, he seems to be leaning to the left if he insists on putting more and more power (which means more and more bureaus, more and more controls, and more and more taxes) into the hands of the central government.

In the matter of tidelands, I merely confirmed to Mr. Porter what I said some years ago after I read the original treaty between Texas and the United States. If you have not taken a look at it, I think you would be interested because—unless

104

my memory fails me—it makes specific mention of tidelands and guarantees their possession to Texas.

Another observation I must make is that any government can start out with the assertion that it is "serving" the people, but a deliberate or accidental development can be that it masters them—if the alleged service involves the building up of bureaus to control remote areas, geographically separated from most of them by hundreds or thousands of miles and completely above or beyond their day-to-day examination and correction.

I think I have no quarrel with your general observations. I merely want to make the point that I am wary of slogans, and if I have a real conviction I am not to be deterred from expressing it merely because I am afraid of how it will read in the headlines. This does not mean that I do not give the most careful consideration to what you and your associates tell me. Normally, I am guided in detail by your counsel, and I shall so continue. But I would be less than frank if I should give you the impression that I intend to tailor my opinions and convictions to the one single measure of net vote appeal. I know, of course, that you have no such thought in mind and I certainly appreciate your spirit of helpfulness and guidance.

I shall be seeing you soon. In the meantime, all the best.

Sincerely,

Dwight D. Eisenhower

Honorable Henry Cabot Lodge, Jr.
Eisenhower for President
Suite 600G, Shoreham Hotel
Washington 8, D. C.

On May 22 the Texas Republican state convention was held at Mineral Wells—an event which profoundly affected the campaign. That Eisenhower had fairly won a majority of Texas delegates was not seriously doubted. The Taft complaint was that these victories were due to Democrats "for the day" coming into the Republican primary, as they had a legal right to do. The Eisenhower men replied that victory in November was impossible without Democrats and that we needed a man who could attract them. Former Governor Hobby's warning about "rough stuff" was well founded: There were reports of some fifty deputy sheriffs being strung across the width of the hall who would not let anyone through who did not wear a Taft button!

Our suspicions alerted, Paul Hoffman spoke to as many journalists as possible about the whole Texas affair. The Mineral Wells convention was covered as no state convention had ever been covered before. As Senator Taft said in his most interesting analysis published seven years later,* "the making of a moral issue out of the Texas case was only possible because every internationalist paper sent special writers to blow up a contest which ordinarily would have excited a few days' interest."

As fast as improprieties were committed, we pamphleteered and propagandized them. The Taft men in Texas had hoped to slide their way through without fuss and bother and seemed dismayed by the publicity.

Brownell observed these gamy proceedings in person. We pondered what to do about them. We well remembered that the first important event at the Democratic Convention of 1932 was Franklin D. Roosevelt's winning a big test vote on the opening day by challenging the seating of the temporary chairman. This was intrinsically a minor matter, but of vast importance psychologically since it gave the Roosevelt forces a roll call vote which they could win at the very outset. It had

* The full text of Senator Taft's analysis is printed in the Appendix.

106

immediately set a psychological tone of Roosevelt victory which never changed.

The proceedings of the 1948 convention showed that the first order of business had been the usual thing—a motion calling for adoption of the rules of the previous convention until permanent rules could be adopted. This would be the first item to which an amendment could be attached. Such an amendment might provide that no contested delegate should vote on any delegate contest until he himself had been lawfully seated.

Brownell had drafted such an amendment and had figured out a number of different ways in which it could be brought up. This proposal later became the "fair play" amendment. Briefly, it said that contested delegates could not vote to seat themselves—or any other contested delegations.

We organized dinners for delegates all over the country—an immense effort—at which the only speech made was an explanation, usually by Brownell, sometimes by me, of the whole Texas affair. We tried to make sure that no delegate could escape hearing the story. To quote Senator Taft's analysis once again, "every Eisenhower delegate knew what his job was."

Brownell finished drafting the "fair play" amendment in June with the help of Ralph Boyd, a Boston lawyer. Credit for the actual name "fair play" goes to Representative Hugh Scott of Pennsylvania,* who did much useful work. Other names such as "no deal" and "clean politics" amendment had been discussed and discarded.

Naturally we wanted as much publicity about the "fair play" amendment as possible. Therefore, three weeks before the convention we announced that a "fair play" amendment would be proposed at the very outset of the proceedings,

* Now the Republican leader of the Senate.

thereby giving public sentiment a chance to build. Neither the Eisenhower nor the Taft camps had ever had enough votes for a first ballot victory. This had become clear as early as March 12, the very day of the New Hampshire primary—and our lowest day—when I sent a memorandum to General Clay, prepared by Mason Sears, collating all of the reports which we had received from each of the forty-eight states and which said:

> There are 1205 convention votes with 603 necessary to nominate.

Taft	600
Eisenhower	469
Warren	76
Stassen	36
McKeldin	24
	1205

> As they stand, these figures mean that General Eisenhower cannot be nominated unless he is given the combined support of Warren, Stassen and McKeldin, whereas Taft can be put across by any single one of them. To get away from a position where any one of these three can throw the nomination to Taft, it will be necessary for the General to gain about 60 votes. The bulk of these could come from Michigan and Pennsylvania.

After March 12 we pulled ahead of Senator Taft, whose strength had diminished, but we were still short of 603. Thus some way had to be found for the Warren, Stassen, and McKeldin forces to join with Eisenhower on something. That way turned out to be the "fair play" amendment.

Plans were also being made and carried out for the return of the general, for the Abilene speech (his first speech since taking off his uniform) and for the roundabout trip which he would take from Abilene to Chicago for the convention.

By early June Eisenhower's popularity had reached an all-time high. The public admired his silent attention to duty while abroad and in uniform. He was, in their eyes, a most unusual sort of candidate with a special kind of prestige. Also, he had just won an impressive series of primary elections. We feared and expected a letdown when he returned to civilian life. We were right. The speech at Abilene sounded dead and uninteresting. It was delivered out of doors in drizzly weather. The onetime supreme commander wore a nondescript raincoat and the wayward breeze mussed his hair—a phenomenon recorded with particular clarity by television. As seen on TV, people on the grandstand were constantly walking to and fro in back of Eisenhower as though nothing important was happening. The ground swell of public opinion which had been building flattened out. As far as opinion was concerned, we were on dead center.

Happily for us, public opinion was not quite as vital as it had been. The delegates had been elected. We knew who they were. Practically every delegate had been talked to and understood what had happened in the "rotten boroughs" of the South. They also knew that Eisenhower was much more popular than Taft. We were thus entering a new and vital phase: the decisions which the delegates would make in Chicago. Other than shaking hands with delegates—and he did some of that—there was nothing much for Eisenhower to do. The time for influencing events by speeches had passed.

On Tuesday, June 26, in Chicago—eleven days before the opening of the convention—we made our first public delegate claim: that Eisenhower would have more than 500 votes on the first ballot—which would be more than Taft would have —and that Eisenhower would win on the second or third ballot. This turned out to have been a modest estimate.

The AP polls gave Taft the edge, which we thought was

wrong. They did not allow for the fact that, unless there is no contest at all, both party conventions usually open with several hundred uncommitted delegates about whom nobody can be sure.

We thought it better to be stronger than we looked! It was desirable for California's Governor Earl Warren, himself a candidate, to think we were a little bit behind Senator Taft. Warren was naturally hoping for a deadlocked convention— and whoever is working for a deadlock tries to help the candidate who is behind.

To get the nomination cinched, Governor Fine of Pennsylvania and Arthur Summerfield would have to come out publicly for Ike. Despite our efforts, both men remained publicly noncommittal to the end. We also tried hard to win the primary in South Dakota before the convention. Although a strong Taft state, we almost carried it. Had we done so, the nomination would have been decided before the convention convened.

A few days before the convention, Guy Gabrielson of the Republican National Committee asked to see Eisenhower. His sole purpose, he said, was to tell Eisenhower of the plans for the designation of the temporary and permanent chairmen and other officials of the convention. Eisenhower saw him at the president of Columbia's house at Morningside Drive in New York at 3:00 P.M. The meeting was attended by Eisenhower and me on the one hand and Gabrielson and Ab Herman, the "political director" of the Republican National Committee, on the other.

It soon became evident that Gabrielson had come as an emissary of Senator Taft's in order to compromise the Texas delegate vote fraud. He said he hoped it would not be necessary "for us to wash our dirty linen in public." I said that those in the Eisenhower movement had no dirty linen to wash, either in public or in private, that the dirty linen had been washed in public at Mineral Wells, Texas, by the Taft people, and that the Republican nomination would not be worth anything unless that was cleaned up.

Gabrielson said, "that is just your opinion" and that "there was plenty of talk that there had been misbehavior on both sides."

I challenged Gabrielson to name one incident of misbehavior in the Eisenhower movement and said that if there was one we would repudiate it immediately. Would the Taft people repudiate what had been done in their name in Texas? This appointment, I said, had been made with Eisenhower on the assumption that it would be solely for the purpose of discussing routine convention appointments and now it appeared that it was going to be turned into an attempt to compromise the Texas vote fraud.

When Gabrielson talked about some of the "reprehensible tactics" of Eisenhower people, Eisenhower bridled. Flushing a bit, he spoke of the smears, many with racist overtones, which were then being uttered against him by supporters of Senator Taft. As a five star general entering his first political contest he was naturally not enjoying the slander of the campaign.

This was all rather unpleasant. But conventions are a grim business.

James Hagerty, Dewey's press secretary, and I arrived in Chicago ten days before the opening of the convention to get statements into the papers as the delegates came to town. Hagerty had enormous talent for press relations, a fertile imagination, and a keen sense of what was news. Our aim was to put out two statements a day—for morning and afternoon papers and their television and radio equivalents. These state-

111

ments tried to impress the public with the activity and general merit of the Eisenhower movement. We hoped that it would be impossible for a delegate to pick up a Chicago paper without reading something about the Ike campaign.

Dated June 20 and sent from the Brown Palace Hotel in Denver came a long letter from the general under the letterhead Office of Dwight D. Eisenhower discussing a TV talk he was planning: "This is to be a thoughtful, studious, but nonetheless very strong presentation of the case for peace and security through cooperation. I shall try to show that this problem will not yield to glittering generalities or loose thinking and that, as a consequence, I can never accept any 'brush off' of the matter in a platform on which I might be expected to stand. You may know that I have already written to Foster Dulles saying that we have got to be very clear and positive on this matter."

This had a great influence on the platform.

A major factor in the fight for the nomination was the twenty-three Republican governors' manifesto in favor of the "fair play" amendment. Without "fair play," said the manifesto, whoever is nominated "will enter a vital and difficult campaign under a serious moral cloud." Worked out by Governors Daniel Thornton of Colorado, Sherman Adams of New Hampshire, and John D. Lodge of Connecticut, it was encouraged by the Eisenhower leaders, but in our wildest dreams we never hoped that all of the Republican governors would agree to it. I doubt whether ever before any meeting of Republican governors had exerted as much influence as was accomplished by this "Houston manifesto."

It offset the lack of support for Eisenhower among Republican senators and representatives. Senator Taft correctly stated, "a majority of Senators and Congressmen were in my favor." Congressman Scott told me in December 1951 that

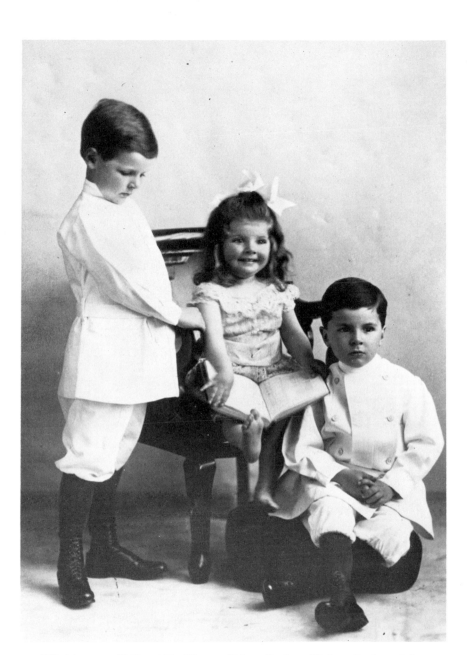

Washington, D.C., 1909. Henry Cabot Lodge, Helena Lodge, John Davis Lodge.

Middlesex School, Concord, Massachusetts, 1920. Middlesex School Debating Team (the author at left, L. B. Lockwood at top, G. R. Perera at right, and A. S. Rogers, bottom).

Louisiana maneuvers, August 1941. Captain Henry Cabot Lodge on active duty.
—Wide World Photo

General Eisenhower visits General de Lattre de Tassigny, commander of the First French Army. The author serves as interpreter.

Lieutenant Colonel Lodge in Germany, February 1945.

Lake Constance, Germany, April 1945. The author and General Jacob L. Devers.

Worcester, Massachusetts, 1946. Emily Sears Lodge with Henry Cabot Lodge.

Two Lodge brothers photographed in Washington, D.C., January 1947. Left, Congressman John Davis Lodge, right, Senator Henry Cabot Lodge.
—*Acme*

1952 campaign, New Bedford, Massachusetts, Congressman Christian A. Herter, General Dwight D. Eisenhower, the author.

Pictured with General Eisenhower in Denver, Colorado, 1952. General Eisenhower inscribed a copy of this photograph: "To: Senator Henry Cabot Lodge, my first 'campaign manager' from his friend, Ike Eisenhower."

At the United Nations Security Council in 1953. The author with Selwyn Lloyd (British Foreign Minister) and Andrei Vishinsky (USSR). Vice-President Nixon, former U.S. Secretary of State James F. Byrnes, and Robert Murphy observe at left.—*The New York* Times

At the United Nations, 1953. Vice-President Nixon, Secretary-General Dag Hammarskjold, Mrs. Vijaya Lakshmi Pandit, and the author.
—*Leo Rosenthal*

At the United Nations, 1953. V. K. Krishna Menon, Ambassador James J. Wadsworth, and the author.

At the Waldorf-Astoria, New York, 1954. President Dwight Eisenhower, arriving for UN visit, with the author.

— *Warman, New York* Herald Tribune

At the New York dinner inaugurating Eleanor Roosevelt Cancer Research Center at Denver, May 23, 1959, the author, Mrs. Roosevelt.
—*Mike Zwerling*

The author with President Harry S. Truman. New York City, 1959.

Photographed in New York City, 1957. Averell Harriman; President Juscelino Kubitschek of Brazil; the author; Governor Thomas E. Dewey; Hugo Goutier, former Brazilian ambassador to UN.

—Leo Rosenthal

Pittsburgh, 1959. Leaving the Carlton House during Khrushchev trip. Man with glasses is U.S. interpreter Alexander Akalovsky; man with black hair and back to camera is Soviet interpreter Viktor M. Sukhodrev; Nikita Khrushchev.

Washington, 1959. The author accompanies Premier Khrushchev to the Lincoln Memorial.

—Burt Glinn, Magnum

Senator Lodge speaks in Beverly, Massachusetts, 1960.
—Life *photo by Bob Gomel*

there were fifty-four members of the House who were for Eisenhower, twenty of whom Scott had talked to himself. I asked Scott how many would be willing to have their names released to the press, saying that there was much good publicity to be had in making their names public, either as a group or separately over a period of time. This never happened. But twenty-eight members of the House said they would accept invitations to make speeches for Eisenhower. About a dozen members of the House and three or four members of the Senate easily found room at a meeting of congressional supporters of Eisenhower in Congressman John Heselton's office in March.

We believed the "Houston manifesto" depressed the Taft camp and led to rumors of compromise. The first suggestion had come from Indianapolis where Senator Taft had told the press that he would be willing to compromise the issue of seating the Texas delegates. We had immediately turned this down. Our rejection caused some press comment, as General Eisenhower, when asked about it, had made some vaguely sympathetic sounds. It appeared to some journalists that the general and his managers disagreed. Actually, it had been understood from the outset between the general and our group that our group was running the campaign. For him suddenly to start managing it would have stultified his basic position that he would not campaign for the nomination.

A second compromise offer came from President Hoover. He had said that there was really not much difference between the two sides in the Texas dispute. I did not want him to think such a thing since he was the only living ex-president and a man for whom I had great respect. So I went to see him in his apartment in the tower of the Waldorf Astoria in mid-June and gave him our view of the Texas situation. He replied that he hoped very much that it could be worked out without

113

a fight or bitterness. Our meeting broke up without a conclusion having been reached, but with a friendly atmosphere.

Then, in Chicago, I received a telegram from the ex-president proposing that a group of three be appointed to settle the dispute. There were to be two "eminent citizens"—neither of whom would be managers—one representing Taft and one representing Eisenhower. The third member would be Mr. Hoover himself. I wrote back—I now think rather stuffily—saying that I could imagine nothing which would be more undemocratic than for any such small group of men to sit down together to decide on the possible disenfranchisement of thousands of voters. Mr. Hoover replied that he "made no suggestion of compromise with evil but a method of arriving at right without emotional trimmings." However, he added, "knowing your zeal I refuse to construe your remarks as an insult to my integrity." There was one more exchange of letters before the last attempt at compromise was made. Later Mr. Hoover referred publicly to his correspondence with me, so that I felt justified in releasing the whole exchange of correspondence.

On Saturday night, July 5, we heard that the Taft-controlled organization charged with the convention schedule was planning to omit from the agenda the motion to adopt temporarily the rules of the previous national convention. This was the motion to which the "fair play" amendment was to be attached and the only way of bringing it up on the opening day. It looked like a body blow at our basic strategy.

It made us wonder whether the opposition was trying to deny us the right to present the "fair play" amendment at all. We were up all Saturday night trying to figure out what the Taft men's game was and what we could do to offset it.

On the telephone we tried to get a group representing all the candidates to go to see Gabrielson in order to make sure that orderly procedure would prevail; but I could not get the group together. So Sunday morning I went alone to Gabrielson's penthouse suite in the Hilton Hotel and got his word that: (1) the Eisenhower speakers would be recognized and would be given an opportunity to present our amendment; (2) we would be given the same amount of time as the Taft speakers; (3) a roll call vote would be taken; and (4) there would be no mumblings at the microphone which could not be heard by the entire convention.

I said that there had been many rumors about the agenda being changed at the last minute, about Eisenhower people not being recognized, about Eisenhower people being denied the use of loud-speakers, and similar tactics. I said to Gabrielson, "If these things happen, the winner of the nomination will have a nomination that is worthless, and those who are responsible for such a miscarriage of the democratic process will lose their reputations."

The methods employed at Mineral Wells, Texas, had alarmed us. We therefore equipped ourselves with fourteen electric bull horns, hastily acquired on Sunday when Governor Dewey had sent an emissary to a bull horn factory in Pennsylvania. They were in the hall ready to be distributed to our floor captains had there been tampering with the microphone system.

Then came the greatest of all attempts at compromise. On Monday morning, July 7, ten minutes before the convention was scheduled to open, Gabrielson telephoned me and asked me to come to his office behind the speaker's platform. I agreed and went alone to Gabrielson's room, where I found Senator William F. Knowland of California, Chairman Gabrielson, and three of Senator Taft's managers—David Ingalls, Representative Clarence Brown of Ohio, and Tom Coleman of Wisconsin.

Senator Knowland, of solemn mien, said that the California

delegation had caucused the night before and had agreed to cast all of its seventy votes in support of the "fair play" motion. But he added that if the result sought by the motion could be achieved in some other way, such a result would "not be inconsistent" with that for which the California delegation had voted. I thought that his statement, with its double negative, was very carefully worded.

Representative Brown, genial and heavy-set, said that the Taft backers would be willing to have the contested delegations agree voluntarily not to vote either in committee or on the floor on any contests until their right to their own seats had been established. In other words, so the argument ran, Brown was offering me precisely what I sought to achieve— but without having a vote about it in the convention.

Chairman Gabrielson, rather owlishly, said he thought it was a wonderful thing for Senator Knowland to seek to arbitrate the dispute and added that certainly the senator was due a great deal of credit if it was possible to work the thing out peaceably.

Thus far I had said nothing except for the usual words of greeting. All through the discussion one theme stood out: how wonderful it would be to compromise and avoid bitterness. There would be no change in the rules and contested delegations would just agree to abstain from voting. But my silence must have indicated my lack of enthusiasm for the idea.

Finally, Ingalls said, "Well, none of you gentlemen has given me a proposition I can take back to Senator Taft." Time was running out; outside of the little office the muffled growlings of the huge crowd could be heard.

At this point I replied, saying that, first of all, I would be willing, as requested, to discuss with my associates any proposal that came to me from Chairman Gabrielson, Senator

Knowland, or Senator Taft. I said I would certainly do so in this case, adding, "I don't think that to have a secret meeting to settle all this is the way to avoid bitterness. The way to avoid bitterness is to vote this up or down on the floor of the convention. The delegates are thoroughly familiar with the question. I have confidence in the delegates."

Then Ingalls asked what was the matter with the proposition. "It gives you everything you want," he said.

I answered, "Well, Dave, if that's true, why doesn't your side accept the 'fair play' amendment?"

Not wanting the Taft forces to accept the "fair play" amendment, I believed that one way to make them feel like refusing was to advise them to accept it.

"You have invited me here," I continued, "to meet three leaders from the Taft headquarters. You gentlemen are thoroughly familiar with this proposition you have made. I've never heard it before. Certainly my first reaction is that it fails to recognize that what we're after is not to gain one or two votes on the Credentials Committee or a handful of votes on the floor. The purpose of the 'fair play' motion is to rehabilitate the Republican party in the eyes of the public and to establish confidence in our procedures."

Gabrielson then asked if the group would reassemble in fifteen minutes, giving me a little time to consult my associates. I never knew whether the Taft people used their control over the doorkeepers to cut me off from my associates, but the fact was that I could not find any of them. Finally, I got Brownell on the telephone at our headquarters back in downtown Chicago. Brownell agreed immediately that the proposition should be turned down.

The opening of the convention was being delayed while all these conversations took place. On my way back to Gabrielson's office, I ran into Barak Mattingly and Representa-

117

tive Christian A. Herter, and took them along to the second meeting. Present were Ingalls, Brown, and Coleman. Neither Knowland nor Gabrielson was there.

Brown opened the conversation by asking Mattingly, "Why are you Dewey people trying to change the rules you made in 1948?"

Mattingly slapped Brown on the back in a friendly gesture and replied, "What are you talking about? Brazilla Carroll Reece made those rules." Reece, a former chairman of the GOP National Committee, was an enthusiastic Taft man.

I said very little at this second meeting, merely commenting, "It's too late to change everything now. I've got to get on the floor and see that Governor Langlie gets recognized." (Arthur B. Langlie was to propose the "fair play" motion.)

Outside, Jack Bell, of the Associated Press, asked Brown what the situation was.

"We're so close together, there's practically no difference at all," said Brown.

I came along right after Brown and said, "There will be no compromise. We'll have a vote on the 'fair play' amendment."

Reaching the floor after the meeting in Gabrielson's office, I went up to the speaker's stand to make sure that the Eisenhower speakers would be recognized. We suspected that the Taft leaders would try to drag out the debate so as to put the vote off until the next day after General Douglas MacArthur's keynote speech which, they might well have hoped, would change some votes in their favor. We insisted on a limit of one hour for each side and would have opposed a greater time limit, even to the extent of forcing the issue of postponement to a roll call vote. Someone with a knowledge of parliamentary procedure had to be present, if the Eisenhower forces were not to be euchred out of having a vote on the opening day. So I went to the rostrum, provoking some booing by suspicious Taft men. We believed the "fair play" amendment would put the opposition into an impossible position from which they could not extricate themselves by any legitimate parliamentary means and that this might lead some hotheads to try illegitimate tactics.

The "fair play" amendment was duly moved. It applied to sixty-eight seats in the convention. We were surprised when Representative Brown, the chief Taft spokesman on the floor, instead of dealing with the main issue—the "fair play" amendment itself—moved to amend it by eliminating seven Louisiana seats which he said had not been under contest before the national committee and thus should not be under contest before the convention.

We wondered why he chose to stand on what was essentially a minor point. Had the Taft forces thought that we would accept the Senator Knowland compromise and were they thus unready when the issue came up before them? We never knew. Besides Representative Brown's speech and the seconding speech, only one other speech in support of the Brown proposal was made—by David Ingalls who said that the seven "should not be removed in a blanket amendment . . . and we should not rely solely upon Senator Lodge, as much as I think of him, to name the delegates to this convention." At this point the official record says, "(Cries of boo.)"

The Brown proposal, an amendment to an amendment, was the first matter to be voted on. The vote on this proposal, therefore, would be the test vote. It was defeated by a roll call vote of 658–548. Then came the victorious vote on the "fair play" amendment itself. This was done on a voice vote, as another roll call was unnecessary. We had won the "fair play" amendment. The possibility of winning the nomination for president seemed suddenly and vividly to open up before us.

As a result of that first victory, the Eisenhower organization won a number of hitherto wavering delegates, acquired sixty-eight freshly seated delegates, identified itself with a good moral cause—"fair play" in politics, established the fact that they had the votes, dominated the next day's headlines, and seized the initiative. This victory was clearly the big event of the day in the minds of the delegates and the press— and not any of the speeches which were made, including General MacArthur's keynote speech that night. We believed that Senator Taft saw immediately that the Monday vote on the "fair play" amendment meant that Eisenhower's nomination was a certainty even though he was not formally nominated until Friday, July 12.

My certainty has grown with the years that any compromise would have lost us the nomination. Eisenhower's demonstrated popularity with all elements of American opinion (particularly with rank and file Republican opinion) and his unique qualifications for the presidency would not have been enough to overcome the ingrained attitudes of many delegates. The Eisenhower candidacy, standing alone, could never have drawn 658 votes. Some other way had to be found to get the delegates to stand together. The "fair play" amendment was it.

I guessed that if Tom Coleman had been the only Taft campaign manager—instead of being one of four—he would have told the Taft delegates to vote for the "fair play" amendment. This would have averted the Taft defeat on the opening day and would have kept the Eisenhower-Taft fight going—with unpredictable consequences.

After the day's doings on the convention floor, Thomas E. Dewey, James H. Duff, Barak T. Mattingly, J. Russel Sprague, Lucius D. Clay, Herbert Brownell, and I gathered in room 1102 of the Hilton to plan for the next day. Also present were Ralph Cake of Oregon, Sinclair Weeks, former senator from Massachusetts, Sherman Adams, governor of New Hampshire, and James Hagerty. When the Credentials Committee was in the limelight, Representatives John Heselton and Christian A. Herter, who became governor of Massachusetts and secretary of state, and Robert Cutler, who became secretary of the National Security Council, were present.

On the mechanical side I had noticed at previous conventions how campaign organizations often worked well in the hotel, but did not function as smoothly at the actual convention hall where it was hard to find each other, general confusion hampered efficient action, and there was no place for quiet thought and for the secret formulation of effective actions. Managers could be seen huddling at the end of a corridor or outside of some telephone booth, amid confusion, interruptions, and eavesdroppings. So we built an air-cooled plywood room. It was erected in the actual building housing the convention hall—the Stockyards Auditorium—in the big concourse outside the second floor gallery. We fitted it out with four desks, telephones, typewriters, and mimeograph machines. This provided a central point of action—for press releases to be turned out and distributed, for storing banners and megaphones, for conferences with floor managers and key delegates, and, above all, a place for connected thought. It was to this room, for instance, that the Minnesota delegation came for the conference before the first ballot.

Construction of this office, with the air conditioning that had to go into it to make it habitable, cost about $8,000. We thought it was worth it. I heard a rumor after the convention was over, that the whole "box" was sold to those supporting the candidacy of Averill Harriman for the Democratic nomination so that actually it cost the Eisenhower group nothing.

121

I believe that such "boxes" have become standard equipment at subsequent conventions of both parties.

Then there was the propaganda battle. As we anticipated, the Taft forces distributed a leaflet, signed by David S. Ingalls, entitled "Stop Dewey," which made the argument that Eisenhower was Dewey's tool. Its opening paragraph read, "Tom Dewey is the most cold-blooded, ruthless, selfish political boss in the United States today. He stops at nothing to enforce his will. His promises are worthless." On Wednesday, July 9, the mellifluous Senator E. M. Dirksen of Illinois in a speech to the convention had said, "Re-examine your hearts before you take this action" (in support of "fair play"). And then, pointing his finger directly at Dewey, added, "Because we followed you before and you took us down the path of defeat." Those who were there will not forget that moment. There was much booing from the galleries. Some delegates went over to Dewey, who was sitting calmly in the front row, and shook their fists in his face.

We, for our part, made maximum use of television * and advertised in the Chicago press, then being read by the delegates. In the heat of controversy I wrote an advertisement myself which gave this argument for the "fair play" amendment:

> The nation may differ as to WHO should be nominated.
> But the nation *agrees* that there must be no shadow of doubt that the winner of the Republican nomination—no matter who he may be—was *honestly* nominated in a free

---

* Mickelson, in *The Electric Mirror*, p. vi, correctly observes that "television played a starring role in a presidential campaign" for the first time in 1952, adding "television suddenly burst upon the American public consciousness in mid-summer 1952 as a major force in the political and governmental processes." I think particularly of the credentials fights at Chicago where we struggled for television coverage.

and *unrigged* convention *by delegates whose right to vote was established beyond question.*

All of us—whether we are for Eisenhower, McKeldin, Stassen, Taft, Warren or anyone else—have the same interest in establishing before the nation the integrity of our Republican procedure.

All of us, therefore, should support the "fair play" amendment—an amendment to the rules providing that no one against whom a contest is pending can vote on any contest, whether in committee or on the floor, until he has been lawfully seated by the convention.

This is a traditional and basic requirement in every popular gathering of free people.

And below was a "box":

You said it, Col. McCormick—in 1912.

"It is, therefore, plain that if . . . contested delegates are seated, they will . . . create a . . . majority . . . composed of delegates improperly seated in violation of good parliamentary law and common morals."

. . . written by Col. Robert R. McCormick in the 1912 convention. William Howard Taft was nominated by the same machine tactics that are at work in Chicago today. He received just 8 electoral votes for the Presidency.

A week before the convention I was in an elevator going to the Ike headquarters on the eleventh floor of the Hilton Hotel when it stopped on the ninth floor, the Taft floor. There all was bustle, noise, banners, and pretty girls. Up on the Eisenhower floor, all was too quiet, orderly, and dignified. I sent a campaign worker over to remedy the situation, which consisted of more pretty girls, more noise, trumpets, and red curtains with gold tassels.

Every day, very slowly, I shoved my way repeatedly through the crowded lobby of the Hilton Hotel, grinning, with gums showing, and shaking hands with everyone I could grab. At the 1932 convention, as a newspaperman, I had admired Jim Farley's same performance for Roosevelt and had marveled at the optimism and trust it engendered. If the campaign manager looked so buoyant, all must be in the bag. And I remembered "Uncle Tom" White's advice at the Massachusetts State Convention in 1936, when I was a candidate for senator, to grin and shake hands in the lobby.

Before making these public appearances Max Rabb would admonish me, "don't look petulant." Priceless advice! Having been going at it with little sleep and indifferent food for nine months I was beginning to get tired—and to look cranky.

The actual balloting for president came on Friday, July 12. On the evening before, Senator Ed Thye of Minnesota and his group came to see me in the "box." Thye did this because I had come up to Governor C. Elmer Anderson of Minnesota on the floor of the convention hall, in full public view, to say that the Eisenhower forces were within striking distance of a first ballot nomination and that I hoped that the Minnesota delegation would be the ones to put it across.

Senator Thye, a tall and quiet man, said to me in his calm and steady manner, "We have been making a count, which is a very accurate count indeed, and we do not find that you have the strength for a first ballot nomination."

In no way daunted I replied, "We think we will have 592 on the first ballot and you know that when a candidate is that strong he is sure to make it on the first ballot."

"We have very accurate facilities for making a count and we don't think you are that strong," Thye said.

I replied, "Ed, you have known me for a long time and you know that I make very careful statements. Last night we had a meeting of sixty of our floor captains in the Stockyards Inn. There is not a delegate among all those twelve hundred who was not known by his or her first name to at least one of those sixty captains. Each one of them stood up and reported individually on the group for which he was responsible. Based on that canvass, we have reached the figure of 592. I believe it is as accurate a figure as is humanly possible."

It was an overcautious estimate. The next day, Friday, July 12, when the balloting for president took place, General Eisenhower received 595 votes to 475 for Senator Taft. Minnesota, followed by many others who changed their vote, put us over the top to a first ballot nomination.

General Eisenhower was the Republican candidate for the presidency of the United States.

The first telephone call which I received on returning to the Hilton was from Eisenhower himself. In his usual polite way he was generous in his praise, even saying that he was "lost in admiration" for the way the campaign had been managed. He had compliments for all of us who had been involved.

His next act was to cross the street from the Blackstone Hotel to the Hilton where he called on Senator Taft. Both men, I am sure, did everything in their powers to persuade their followers not to bear grudges because of the hard blows struck in the heat of political combat.

The general then went on to his election campaign and I returned to Massachusetts to run for re-election against an up and coming young congressman named John F. Kennedy.

It is still too soon to evaluate what the eight years of Eisenhower's tenure meant to the country. There was peace—more than we had had before. There was prosperity. The Republican party in 1952, for the first time in twenty hopeless years, became competitive—and is still so today.

He decided against trying a military solution in Vietnam.

He opposed the use of force at Suez in 1956, pressing hard for a cease-fire and withdrawal there, and played a leading part in creating the UN force which kept peace in the Middle East for eleven years. He deplored the Soviet seizure of Hungary, but believed that it was so close to the Soviet Union that we could take no effective steps without unconscionable risk. He put U.S. troops into Lebanon, took them out, and thus warded off the attempt to subvert the Lebanese government—and did so without the loss of one single life. He understood the use of force, having wielded more of it than anyone else ever has. His invitation to Khrushchev to visit the United States was an event of far-reaching influence.

He was dubious about the claim that "big government" or "socialism" could bring the millennium. He made progress in the field of civil rights, believing that, in the end, while legislation was indispensable, the promptings of people's hearts would be decisive. Richard Rovere says that "Eisenhower's only first-class domestic problem was Senator McCarthy and he finally managed to get on top of that one."

Some other things stand out with clarity: his good humor, his common sense, his insights about problems, his clear and penetrating mind, his intuition about people, his capacity to lead, the way in which his personality improved the tone of our public life, and his shining integrity. Was he an intellectual? or a conservative? or a liberal? He defied such classification, but goodness emanated from him.

It was his amalgam of traits and achievements which led to his being actually drafted for president. Of what other man in the twentieth century can that be said? That is what makes his story unique.

CHAPTER FOUR

☆ ☆ ☆ ☆ ☆ ☆ ☆ ☆ ☆ ☆

The Cabinet and
the United Nations

In November 1952, I was defeated for a fourth term
in the Senate by that very prepossessing man John F. Kennedy,
which hastened me off to the Caribbean to lick my wounds.
Defeat is never a pleasure and at the time one's ego needs
soothing. So, when I received the ensuing two messages I was
inordinately pleased.

First came this telegram from Eisenhower:

NEW YORK, N.Y

THE COUNTRY HAS LOST A GREAT OPPOR-
TUNITY TO KEEP A REAL STATESMAN IN THE
SENATE. NEVERTHLESS THERE IS STILL LOTS
OF WORK TO DO.

DWIGHT D. EISENHOWER

127

Then this letter from General Marshall:

Dear Lodge:
I am terribly sorry that the electorate failed you in your state. They made a great error for you were among the most conspicuous statesmen in public office. I anticipated great things for you and maybe in the curious workings of fate this mishap may be a turn for greater things.
Personally, I want to see you Secretary of State preferably. If not, then Secretary of Defense. Some one tells me you came out against any cabinet position. I hope not. If ever the country needed a man it needs you!
Faithfully yours,
G. C. Marshall

My Caribbean outing over, I met the president-elect in Washington and went with him to the White House for a conference with President Truman at which Secretary of State Acheson, in a lucid and comprehensive report on the Korean war, told us that a number of the Chinese communist prisoners in our custody had made it vociferously clear that they did not wish to return to mainland China. The Truman policy was against sending them there if they did not want to go. In the Eisenhower administration the issue was eventually settled by both sides adhering to the principle of freedom of choice whereby some of the Chinese went to Taiwan, more went to the mainland, and about a dozen Americans went to the mainland (most of whom have since returned).

The president-elect asked me to take charge of the transition (except for budgetary matters) from the outgoing Truman administration to Eisenhower's incoming one. This meant putting the newly designated heads of the government agencies in touch with the outgoing ones—to find out what they thought were the most pressing questions in each agency

128

so that the president-elect could get an over-all picture. Korea turned out to be the most pressing topic.

A few days after his inauguration, the president appointed me United States representative to the United Nations, and made me a member of the cabinet. He said he wanted me to take the post at the UN because of his concern over the American public's lack of enthusiasm for the UN. He wanted an active debater so that whenever the Soviet representative —the late Andrei Vishinsky—made one of his abusive tirades against us, there would be a prompt and factual American answer. Ignoring the Soviet attack or answering it four days later, he thought, weakened our influence. He hoped the American reply would be published in the same newspaper edition as the Soviet attack * and he assumed that my experience in the Senate and on the stump would stand me in good stead. My French and some fairly convincing noises which I could make in a few other languages were also helpful. Being a member of the cabinet gave me a bit more prestige at the United Nations, where I could now be Monsieur le Ministre as well as Monsieur l'Ambassadeur.

Eisenhower's conduct of his cabinet † meetings was anything but dull. On his desk was the motto *Suaviter in modo*,

---

* This view was evidently shared by Senator Taft who, with his typical generosity, wrote me on April 8, 1953: "I congratulate you on the effective manner in which you presented your arguments, and even more on the promptness of your reply to the Russian attack on our Army."

† The cabinet "is today an extralegal creation, functioning in the interstices of the law, surviving in accordance with tradition, and institutionalized by usage alone," R. F. Fenno, Jr., *The President's Cabinet* (Cambridge, Mass.: Harvard University Press, 1959). In a letter to me dated April 29, 1957, the secretary of the cabinet, Maxwell M. Rabb, said, "the Cabinet is created by the President and consists of whoever he wants to appoint to it. Unlike the Security Council, which is cre-

fortiter in re ("flexible in method, unyielding on substance")
attributed to Claudio Aquaviva, general of the Jesuits in
1606. This was the key to his general approach. Then there
was his admonition, "Remember, you're not important, but
your job is." His obvious approval and enjoyment of the few
heated arguments between cabinet members; his frustration
when there was no such clash, as at sessions of the National
Security Council where participants droned on from carefully hedged position papers; and his warning that *plans* were
usually worthless when the crunch came, but that the act of
planning was vital—all these things made these meetings
interesting.

I was at the UN from January 1953 to September 1960.
Most of my instructions came from the State Department except in such crises as Suez, Hungary, Guatemala, Lebanon,
and the Congo, when there was also a lively presidential reaction—sometimes by written message, sometimes by telephone.
The Suez and Hungarian crises, both happening at about
the same time, were the most difficult and trying of my experiences at the United Nations. It all started on the night of
October 29, 1956. I was at the opening of the Metropolitan
Opera, attired in white tie and tails. Sir Pierson Dixon, the
British ambassador, was in a box close by. During the second
act, James W. Barco, the hard-driving minister at the United
States Mission, called me into the lobby to say that we had
just received word from Washington that the British and
French governments had delivered an ultimatum to Egypt
and Israel that they were planning an occupation within
twelve hours of the Suez Canal Zone and that Washington

ated by statute, the Cabinet has never been either created or defined
by statute. It is not mentioned in the Constitution."

had instructed me to ask for an immediate meeting of the Security Council.

As Sir Pierson was also a member of the Security Council, I asked him to leave his box—then told him what had happened. On hearing that the British were planning to invade Egypt, his naturally ruddy face turned white. Evidently he knew nothing about it. When I said that I was instructed to call a meeting of the Security Council for that night, he expressed regret. He seemed deeply moved. The next day he told me that if the bombardment of Port Said continued, he personally would resign. (It did not continue.) He and I, as representatives of allied governments which were in deep disagreement, were opposing each other in the open forum of the UN. It was enough to strain, if not to rupture, friendly relations, but when he left the UN in 1960, he sent me a letter saying, "Ours has been an association which I shall certainly never enjoy again in the line of business and friendship." And I felt the same.

This was the beginning of a period of tension which lasted in its most strenuous form for about a month, as at this same time the Russians also invaded Hungary. A session on Suez adjourning at midnight would be followed by one on Hungary convening at 1:00 A.M. Sleep, if any, came from cat naps on the office sofa.*

During these tense days the UN created the United Nations Emergency Force, composed of soldiers from many nations, which went to the Palestine area (the Gaza Strip, the Straits of Sharm el Sheik, and along the demarcation line) to keep the adversaries apart. It kept the peace for eleven years

* With the indispensable help of a brilliant and tireless staff we were also handling the Algerian question, the Cyprus question, and the Kashmir dispute—all at the same time.

131

—a unique feat. It was an elaborate and ambitious device which in quiet times would have caused years of discussion —and not much by way of result. For this noteworthy achievement the Canadian secretary of state for external affairs and recipient of the Nobel Peace Prize, Lester B. Pearson, has rightly been given the lion's share of the credit. Some understanding of all that was involved in his achievement is given by the following background:

The first evening after the invasion, the U.S. State Department sent up a draft of a resolution (written, I suspect, by Joseph J. Sisco, the present assistant secretary of state for Near Eastern affairs) which in effect created this force. My instructions, very wisely, were not to sponsor the resolution myself, but to find the member of the Assembly whom I considered the most competent—the most likely to get quick action—and to get him to sponsor it. The choice of the man was left to me. The names of two men came immediately to mind: Mr. Pearson of Canada and Ambassador Joao Carlos Muniz of Brazil. I walked out of my office into the broad corridor and by the merest chance bumped into Mr. Pearson. I gave him the text of the resolution and said that the United States government hoped he would sponsor it.

His clear and penetrating mind quickly grasped the significance of the paper and he immediately agreed to sponsor it, without the usual time-consuming changes of commas here and words there. He seemed to see in a flash, while we were standing there, how much the cause of peace would be helped by his sponsoring a resolution to which the United States was already committed. This would assure not only U.S. support, but also the support of the many members who then looked to us for leadership. Had he decided to sponsor an individual resolution of his own, it would not have had such great momentum behind it at the outset and might have consumed much more precious time.

Accordingly he went directly downstairs to the Assembly Hall and succeeded in getting recognized—no mean feat. When I got back to my office a minute or so later, I heard his voice coming over the loud-speaker defending and explaining the resolution. Due to his perspicacity and leadership a new step was taken in peace-keeping which under ordinary conditions would have taken years of arguing and pettifogging.

An especially able Western European statesman at the United Nations at that time was Paul Henri Spaak of Belgium. During the hectic days of late October and early November 1956 we were trying to bring about an immediate cease-fire and withdrawal from Egypt of all foreign troops. A resolution was before us in the General Assembly which would have required these troops to withdraw "forthwith." Mr. Spaak moved an amendment to the pending resolution which, he said, would change the words so as simply to enable the foreigners to "save their face" and would enable them to support a cease-fire and a withdrawal without losing too much "prestige." He and the British had apparently been led to believe that the U.S. would support his proposal.

We in the U.S. Mission in New York thought the Spaak amendment was more than a minor change and that it would make it possible for the foreigners to stay on indefinitely. My instructions were to get a cease-fire and withdrawal as quickly as possible. I had stated that the failure of the foreigners to order their armed forces to cease hostilities was "most discouraging." We believed that the call which the General Assembly had already made was "unconditional," that it should not be weakened, and that fighting must cease immediately.

133

In fact I called President Eisenhower on the telephone during the evening (Secretary Dulles was in the hospital) and there was absolutely no doubt that he considered the situation brought about by the presence of invading troops to be dangerous and to require immediate action. In my conversation with the president I specifically raised the question of the Spaak amendment and he authorized me to abstain.

In his book, *Unfinished Struggles,* Mr. Spaak, after describing the situation, made this observation:

> Cabot Lodge is an American who speaks French admirably. This trait has given him the reputation of being pro-European. I have often asked myself whether this was justified. On this occasion, at any rate, he not only did not show solidarity with France and England, but he showed a hostility which is very difficult to justify since it was only a question of a few wounding words without changing the essence of the recommendation.
>
> Did he act on his own authority or was he following instructions from Washington? I do not know. It is said that Selwyn Lloyd (British Foreign Minister) did not forgive him for his attitude. If I had been in his place, I would certainly have had the same feeling. As for me, although I was not directly involved, I was made indignant by this inexplicable way of acting.
>
> My amendments were rejected by a vote of 32 to 23 and 18 abstentions among which was the United States. It is more than probable that if Cabot Lodge had intervened to make a plea for this modification, the result would have been different.
>
> At the moment this vote was perhaps not important since the French and British had decided to withdraw their troops, but the attitude of the Americans on the Suez question was to become one of the elements of French anti-Americanisms—and de Gaulle made the most of it.

Mr. Spaak's remark invites the comment that at no time did I act on my own authority. Everything I did was in accordance with instructions from Washington and with the president's policy of disspelling a threat to the peace—not just a question of eliminating "a few wounding words." Also, fluency in a foreign language does not comport automatic agreement with whatever at any given moment happens to be the politics of the several governments which speak that language. But such fluency has in my case led to admiration and affection for the countries where the language is spoken.

Not long after my encounter with Mr. Spaak I was instructed to try to bring about the passage of a resolution requiring the placement of the recently created United Nations Emergency Force on the Egypt-Israel demarcation line. Such a resolution was necessary because, no nation ever having ceded any sovereignty to the UN, the UN had no sovereignty. Consequently, it could not place its forces anywhere without the consent of the country where the forces were to go. The force had been created; but, without further specific action by the UN, it could not go anywhere.

In January 1953 there were fifty-six members in the United Nations. If we were trying to get a two-thirds vote—which the charter requires for anything "important"—we could usually count on fourteen from the North Atlantic countries and members of the British Commonwealth, plus nineteen from Latin America, making a total of thirty-seven, or two-thirds of fifty-six. This was easy. By 1956 the membership had grown to seventy-three and it was impossible to get forty-nine votes simply by adding together the NATO countries, the Latin American countries, Liberia, and our three good friends in East Asia—Formosa, the Philippines, and Thailand.

Realizing the difficulty of obtaining a two-thirds vote, I started to look for members who would help. One member who had a constituency in the General Assembly was the voluble representative of India, Mr. Krishna Menon. I therefore began marathon negotiations with him, realizing that his support would mean the adherence of countries which are variously described as "neutralist" or "nonaligned." Their votes, added to those which we already had, would be enough to bring about the adoption of our resolution by a two-thirds vote.

Our conversations were arduous. He would propose language which, to me, robbed the text of any meaning whatever. I suppose he thought that I was obdurate. Several times I said that I could see very little use in talking any more and, at least twice, I rose to leave the table. Finally, we agreed on language which did make it possible to place the United Nations Emergency Force in the area. The language had been so worked over by Mr. Menon and by me that it probably would not have passed muster at an English composition course at any respectable college. But we were both able to interpret it so that we could stand on it.

Here—in all their stylistic awkwardness and turgidity—are the key words: "the scrupulous maintenance of the Armistice Agreement requires the placing of the United Nations Emergency Force on the Egyptian-Israel armistice demarcation line and the implementation of other measures as proposed in the Secretary-General's report, with due regard to the considerations set out therein with a view to assist in achieving situations conducive to the maintenance of peaceful conditions in the area."

Only with such elliptical language are many diplomatic settlements possible. The resolution passed the General Assembly on February 2, 1957, and formed the basis for stationing the Emergency Force on the Gaza Strip, at the Straits of Sharm el Sheikh, and on the demarcation line, where it remained for about eleven years—and there was no war. It is disheartening to think that eleven years later the force was pulled out—and that once more there was bloodshed. The U.S. believed that the force should remain until its task was completed and that it should be withdrawn only after there had been ample opportunity for consideration by the General Assembly.*

Krishna Menon was undoubtedly a blunt talker, but then, so was I on occasion. Everything I have learned since has convinced me that over the years he was always faithfully carrying out Prime Minister Nehru's instructions and was not, as many thought, voicing his personal anti-Americanisms. This resolution marked the only time during our service together that he ever made a promise to me or that I made him one. He kept his word—and I kept mine. With men who keep their word (and both have the same understanding of the words which are used) much can be accomplished, however much disagreement there may be on things in general.

In June 1958 Lebanon was the dilemma. The United States was convinced that there existed outside interference in the internal affairs of the Republic of Lebanon, and that this

---

* In *Khrushchev Remembers* (Boston and Toronto: Little, Brown and Company, 1970), pp. 450–51, Nikita S. Khrushchev says, "It's not at all clear to me why Egypt demanded that U Thant remove the U.N. troops from the border between Egypt and Israel. These forces were a restraining influence on the Israeli aggressors. They were helping to neutralize the threat of a clash. . . . I remember we voted in favor of sending a U.N. peace keeping force to the Near East in order to prevent war from breaking out between the two hostile states, Egypt and Israel. It's simply incomprehensible to me why Egypt demanded that these forces be removed."

interference promoted civil strife and hampered the efforts of the authorities to restore order. This interference in Lebanon's internal affairs, we then believed, came from the United Arab Republic. We also thought there were infiltrations from Syria. These incursions had fomented violence and bloodshed.

The State Department thought that this was part of an organized campaign aiming not only at Lebanon, but also at the Kingdom of Jordan, and that much of it stemmed from the same people who had brutally overthrown the legally established government of Iraq and had assassinated its prime minister, Nuri Said. We were, at the time, ignorant of what we have since learned: that the United Arab Republic had nothing to do with the Iraqi revolution and that Mr. Gamal Abdel Nasser had been as surprised as everyone else.

The situation grew so bad that President Eisenhower gave serious consideration to the request of the president of Lebanon for help—and in July he responded by landing American troops on the beach in Lebanon.

Before this step was taken, I was called to Washington for a Sunday conference with Secretary John Foster Dulles and his brother, Allen, the head of the Central Intelligence Agency. We knew that the action contemplated by the president would arouse strong feelings at the United Nations. Dag Hammarskjold's anger at a private meeting with me after the landing of troops was indeed memorable. When I came into his office his face first became pink and then flushed to red as he told me how much he deplored what we had done and how dangerous he thought it was. Hostile speeches were surely to be expected. Wanting to make the best possible defense, I asked our intelligence officials to give me the names of a few Egyptians or Syrians who were interfering in the internal affairs of Lebanon and the names of the places where they had been found. I was surprised to learn that such information was not available.

Washington's deep conviction that there was a plot on foot to subvert Lebanon was based, in large part, on the organized threats of assassination of top Lebanese officials which reached the president of Lebanon by telephone and which caused him to ask for our help.

Thus, in contemplating the Security Council meeting on the morning of July 15, I was more perplexed than I had ever been at the United Nations—before or since—on just how to deal with the problem. I had no proof of interference. I decided to base my case on generalities.

I was thinking about those things at breakfast on the morning of July 15 when, at 8:00 A.M. the telephone rang. It was Secretary Dulles in Washington, obviously perturbed. He began by asking me how I was feeling, as one might ask a prize fighter about to step into the ring. I told him that I felt fine and then outlined what I was planning to say. He then said that he had just learned from a dependable source that the ambassador of Iraq to the United Nations, Mr. Fadil al-Jamali, had been assassinated in Iraq. Mr. al-Jamali was a good friend and a jovial soul. I was shocked. Then, thinking of the Security Council session fixed for 10:00 A.M., I asked Secretary Dulles if I could announce this deplorable event in the debate. It would dramatically support our contention that violence and assassination were at large in the Arab world. Secretary Dulles said that I could.

When the Security Council meeting opened, I began,

Mr. President:

The Council meets today to confront difficulties as serious as any in its history.

The territorial integrity of Lebanon is increasingly threatened by insurrection, stimulated and assisted from outside.

Plots against the Kingdom of Jordan, which have become evident over the past few months, are another sign of serious instability in the relations between nations in the Middle East.

And now comes the overthrow—in an exceptionally brutal and revolting manner—of the legally established Government of Iraq. I have just heard this morning, Mr. President, before coming over here, of the murder of our esteemed and popular colleague here in the United Nations from Iraq—Mr. Fadil al-Jamali. Only a few weeks ago he was here with us. We heard his voice; we rejoiced in his humor; we were heartened by his fellowship. Now we learn that he was not only murdered; but that his body was actually dragged through the streets of Baghdad. Decent people throughout the world, wherever they may be, will recoil at this monstrosity.

In all these circumstances, the President of Lebanon has asked, with the unanimous authorization of the Lebanese Government, for the help of friendly governments so as to preserve Lebanon's integrity and independence.

I pointed at Mr. al-Jamali's empty chair.

Imagine my confusion and surprise when, a few days later, I discovered that Mr. al-Jamali was not dead! It appeared that he had had a double, and that it was the double who had been killed and whose body had been dragged through the streets. Apparently, when Mr. al-Jamali had been prime minister of Iraq he had closed down the brothels in Baghdad, thus infuriating the prostitutes. When violence and disorder started, these ladies took advantage of the opportunity to revenge themselves. Mr. al-Jamali's unfortunate double paid the price.

The Soviet representative, Ambassador Arkady Sobolev, a cool and affable descendant of czarist civil servants, rejoiced over the error! He produced a photograph of Mr. al-Jamali in obvious good health and repeated bits of my rhetoric on the opening day of the debate.

Our troops stayed until September when the Lebanese government felt itself no longer threatened by externally inspired subversion. We accordingly pulled our troops out— without the loss of a single life. The Soviet Union withdrew their resolution criticizing the United States for having intervened.

The various conflicts which arise in the Middle East are extremely painful, not only to the people in the area, but to all others involved. Some Middle Eastern governments, however much they may differ on most issues, seem sometimes to have in common a desperate compulsion to injure their enemy regardless of the greater injury they may bring upon themselves.

The story is told of the scorpion on the bank of the Nile who wanted to get across but could not swim. He sees a frog nearby and asks the frog to take him over on his back. The frog says, "I would be crazy to do that because you will kill me." The scorpion answers, "Of course, I won't kill you because I cannot swim and if I kill you, then I drown." So the scorpion gets on the frog's back and when they are in midstream, the scorpion bites the frog in the back of the neck. Just before the frog dies he says to the scorpion, "Why did you do it?" and the scorpion answers, "This is the Middle East."

Arnold J. Toynbee writes that the Israeli achievement has already been justified by its results: It has transformed the country for the better out of all recognition. Truly a stupendous achievement. But, he adds, the tragic misfortune of Israel is that the Arab population has not been conciliated.

One feels that there is tragedy on all sides. In his book, *Bitter Lemons*, Lawrence Durrell speaks of that wonderful

Moslem quality called *kayf*—"the contemplation which comes of silence and ease . . . not meditation or reverie, which presupposes a conscious mind relaxing . . . something deeper, a fathomless repose of the will which does not even pose to itself the question: 'Am I happy or unhappy?' "

What a salutary exercise that would be!

On being appointed to the United Nations, I had been thoroughly briefed by the State Department on past attempts of foreign spies to penetrate our official secrets, in particular, attempts by the Soviets to penetrate Western embassies in Moscow. Just after World War II, there had been an expert in the British embassy in Moscow who had arranged a microphone so that it would break the eardrum of any of the Soviets who might be listening. I was also briefed about the visit of Prime Minister MacMillan to the Soviet Union in 1959 when a specially prepared tent had been set up in the embassy ballroom and surrounded by busy typists. The rattle of typewriters made it impossible for the Soviet microphones to pick up what was being said inside the tent into which Prime Minister MacMillan and his advisers would crawl everyday in order to have a secure conversation.

In particular, I was told about a British radio expert who, from his office in the British Embassy, while "cruising" one day on his radio set, was startled to hear the voice of the American ambassador George Kennan dictating his mail. Apparently the Soviet spies had succeeded in introducing a microphone into Ambassador Kennan's office. After the British reported this to us, our security experts went to work to try to find the microphone. First, they shredded the ambassador's desk into small splinters, but found nothing. Then they scraped all the plaster off the walls right down to the bare brick. I have seen the photographs. But they still found nothing. Finally, someone thought of a plaque some eighteen inches in diameter, bearing the seal of the United States, which hung on the wall in back of the ambassador's chair. Someone split the plaque along its edge and found that it was hinged and could open out. Inside the plaque, under the beak of the eagle, was a microphone about two inches long and three-quarters of an inch wide. It was so sensitive that a powerful radio beam directed from a beacon a few miles away would enable everything to be heard. To cap the story, the plaque had been given to the ambassador by a society for Soviet-American friendship. Beware of gifts!

I had forgotten about this until early in 1960 when our U-2 plane was shot down over the Soviet Union. This caused an uproar and was given as the reason for the cancellation of President Eisenhower's scheduled trip to the Soviet Union. Righteous indignation filled the air at the UN. Ambassador after ambassador expressed his deep sense of shock at our flying over Russia, although many of them remarked to me in private what a wonderful engine the U-2 plane must have had and how fantastic the camera must have been. To climax the indignation, the Soviet Union introduced a resolution condemning the United States for aggression. This was but one of the many consequences of the U-2 incident, which was marked in September by Chairman Khrushchev of the Soviet Union (who had made his American tour the year before) banging his desk with his shoe.

It was my job to defend the U.S. against the Soviet resolution. A very few minutes convinced me that it would not be wise or successful to attempt a legal argument. The best we could do would be to show that the Soviets had spied on us and then ask, "What kind of justice is it which says that it is right for the Soviets to spy on us, but it is wrong for us to take measures to protect ourselves?"

At this point Christian Herter, then secretary of state, kindly offered me the plaque with the eagle on it. I accepted with alacrity and it was sent up from Washington to New York in a big black leather case. Four days went by before the moment came in the debate when it was germane to present the eagle. Finally the witching hour arrived, and the plaque was whisked out from under my desk where it had been, in anticipation. We put it on the desk and opened it so that I could point to the microphone under the eagle's beak. The uproar was gratifying. Even the Russians could not help but smile.

Their resolution was voted down and the meeting adjourned just before lunch. On the way out of the Security Council chamber I asked Anatoly F. Dobrynin, now the Soviet ambassador in Washington and then an assistant secretary-general at the United Nations, why they had charged us with aggression, since obviously one man in a single airplane armed only with a pistol could not possibly commit an aggression. "Why," I asked, "did you of the Soviet Union not charge us with trespassing? Had you done this, you would have caught us where we were clearly in the wrong." Dobrynin's answer was that the word for "aggression" and for "trespass" is one and the same in Russian.

That particular Thursday happened to be the day of the monthly Security Council lunch—which I always attended. I was seated between Andrei Gromyko, the Soviet foreign minister, and Ambassador Sobolev of the Soviet Union. During a pause in the conversation, Sobolev said to me in a voice loud enough to be heard by all, "The next time we put one of those Soviet-American friendship plaques in the ambassador's office, we will put the microphone under the eagle's tail."

It is encouraging that the United Nations can play a part

as a restorer of perspective and of relative calm, as it did in this case.

Many years spent in various forums have convinced me that for professional adversaries to dislike each other personally can only do harm and introduce an element of animus into the work, which hampers the achievement of peaceful settlements. The opponent of today is often the helpful colleague of tomorrow.

For instance, Mr. Dobrynin collected instances in history of Russian-American cooperation, so I told him of a book I had read by R. Ernest Dupuy about First Lieutenant George Washington Whistler of the class of 1819 at West Point, who had in 1842, at the personal request of the czar of Russia, left the United States to construct the St. Petersburg (Leningrad)-Moscow railway. He died in Russia as the work was nearing completion. He was the father of the famous painter, James Abbott McNeill Whistler. I received this letter from Ambassador Dobrynin shortly thereafter:

16 March 1959

Dear Mr. Ambassador,

Your information about Lieutenant Whistler and his work in Russia contains completely new facts for me. I have checked with materials that I had, but could not find anything on this subject.

I think it is an interesting but generally unknown episode of Russian-American relations in the past.

I am very grateful to you for the possibility of being acquainted with these interesting facts which will be useful to me.

Yours sincerely,
Anatoly F. Dobrynin
Under-Secretary

The spring of 1960 was, however, far from friendly. To the sessions on the U-2 plane were added sessions on the shooting down by the Soviet Union of the U.S. Air Force plane RB47 over the international waters of the White Sea. This session was made especially poignant by the presence of the families of the plane's crew who sat in the gallery of the Security Council chamber during the whole debate. Then came sessions on the Cuban complaint against us, which were followed by decisions for UN action in the Congo. These decisions required the creation of a UN force to prevent armed personnel under communist control, which we believed to be working in neighboring countries, from bringing about a big power confrontation in the Congo. All this somber and exciting stuff was extensively covered on television and seen by large audiences, which, as will appear, had some bearing on my getting the Republican nomination for vice-president.

The Japanese diplomats of an earlier day would not talk business until the third visit. The first two were for hospitality, to establish an atmosphere of pleasantness. Today's international problems are so complicated, the world is so dangerous, and emotions are often so bitter that one thinks with admiration of this old Japanese custom. All too often our diplomats, instead of having two visits for hospitality, rush to a meeting two or three hours after getting out of an airplane which, by passing through five or six time zones, has totally upset their circadian rhythm. They sleep in the daytime and lie awake at night. They are "disoriented," which brings me to the larger aspect.

Hospitality still plays a tremendous role in diplomacy in establishing an atmosphere of pleasantness—and nowhere more so than at the United Nations. As the UN is in the U.S., it seemed to me imperative to invite the ambassadors of the foreign countries represented at the United Nations to lunch or dinner at the residence of the American representative (as representative of the "host country").

Also every nation represented at the United Nations has a national Day, of which two examples are our Independence Day and France's Bastille Day. The American representative should always go to such celebrations, hopefully having his picture taken with the host.

Entertaining can be used as an opportunity for winning people over to one's own government's point of view or, at least, of achieving a better understanding of it. Many representatives, particularly from small countries, were, when I was there, only vitally interested in two or three questions and were quite free to vote on other matters as their judgment dictated. If they came to one's home in a convivial manner and were given convincing arguments for our policies, much good could ensue.

Soon after our arrival we discovered that international parties where people of many different countries are gathered may be awfully stiff. Music is the answer, as it covers a multitude of silences, for which everybody is grateful. There was a marvelous and never fatigued accordion player and pianist, "Nicky," who could play music from every part of the world. This would often lead to singing. I remember a duet between Governor Dewey and the Japanese ambassador! My colleague, Ambassador James J. Wadsworth, in addition to his forensic ability, was one of the most naturally musical men I have ever known. He would sing, accompanying himself with his guitar, entrancing all who heard him and making friends for the U.S.A. in the bargain. At times I was known to render a simple ditty entitled "You Can Easily See She's Not My Mother," sometimes doing it in five languages, like a parrot.

Senator Lyndon B. Johnson of Texas, chairman of the

Senate subcommittee on appropriations,* which included the U.S. Mission to the UN, had a real understanding of the problems which the United States faced at the United Nations. He also was much interested in outer space. When some questions relating to outer space came up in the United Nations, I invited him to come to New York and take part in the debate. He had a press conference while there which was attended by the broad spectrum of journalists of every color, from every clime who cover the UN. One African journalist asked a question bearing on civil rights which inspired Senator Johnson to make a statement on the importance of treating every man fairly regardless of his color. At the end of this statement Senator Johnson concluded, "Those are my convictions and if I am not always true to them, I hope I'll end up in the ashcan."

A correspondent of the London Times in his best British manner turned to the correspondent of the Indianapolis News and remarked, "When he says 'ashcan,' does he mean 'dust bin?' "

His visit was a great success and a help from many points of view.

Let us now look at the pluses and the minuses of the UN:

In the past twenty-five years the UN, in addition to the crises in Suez and Lebanon already mentioned, also gave important help in these situations: the withdrawal of foreign troops from Iran in 1947; the communist withdrawal from Greece in 1949; resisting the aggression in Korea in 1950;

---

* The current appropriation for all expenses of the U.S. Mission to the UN when I took over in January 1953 was $957,500 and a request was pending for an increase to $1,056,000. I brought it down to $819,000—$237,000 below the request of the previous administration. Personnel was reduced from 143 to 105—and, I think, efficiency increased.

148

cease-fires or truces in Indonesia, Kashmir, and Cyprus; preventing the Congo from becoming a cause of confrontation between the great powers in 1960; and ushering the erstwhile colonies of Africa into the family of nations. (Because of the increase in the neutralist or nonaligned vote, it would be next to impossible now for the UN to act in the same way with respect to these situations, were they to reappear. This is because many new members either respond directly to the Soviet view or, to say the least, have no interest in the traditional Western view that the UN's chief purpose is "peace keeping"—or else, they consider that the UN's chief value is as a forum for anticolonialism.)

The first priority at the UN is peace and security, as in the instances covered in the preceding paragraph. The second, far ahead of any other, should be economic and social development. Along these lines, the United Nations Development Program, under the remarkable and devoted leadership of onetime Marshall Plan administrator Paul Hoffman, by preinvestment surveys and technical education, has advanced the fundamentals of a good life: food, shelter, health, and education. Because it is done multilaterally (many nations working together) rather than bilaterally (one country working with one other country alone), $1.00 of input by the United States, for instance, generates more than $6.00 worth of actual development work. Thus our proportion gets smaller and the recipient nations' proportion gets greater because the UN Development Program gets more and more people into the act. Much, but not all, of our own bilateral AID program for economic and social development abroad could, I believe, be channeled through UN agencies, with advantage to us as well as to the recipient nations.

The United States has a creditable record at the United Nations concerning disarmament. Bernard Baruch's proposal

149

for an atomic development authority and the Acheson-Lillienthal proposal for internationalizing fissionable material both had great merit and could have changed the course of history for the better had they been adopted. President Eisenhower's initiatives—the Atoms for Peace proposal in 1953, the open skies proposal in 1955, as well as the later negotiations for a test ban and for a nonproliferation treaty—were most constructive. Continuing in this line, and carrying it still further, were the treaties curbing the arms race concluded with the Soviet Union by President Nixon.

The internationalization of atomic development as a step toward disarmament and peace is an attractive idea. In this connection I recall that the former president of Williams College, James P. Baxter, wrote that in the 1780s Maryland refused to accept the Articles of Confederation unless all the states possessing claims to Western lands would agree to pool them for the nation's good. "Every school boy knows," says Baxter, "that the joint ownership of the Western lands by the thirteen seaboard states set in motion centrifugal forces that helped to give us a more perfect union. Is it farfetched," he asks, "to believe that the internationalization of atomic development might have a similar beneficent effect on world affairs, allaying suspicions, mitigating rivalries, lifting the world to the level of amity and concord? It would be a first step toward common control of common property—a strange type of property—with a fabulous potential for good or evil."

So much for the pluses. There are also some undeniable minuses:

With the advantage of hindsight, one can now say that much trouble would have been avoided if, before the French left Indochina, President Truman had asked the United Nations in the early 1950s to intervene—somewhat as it did in the Congo in 1960—as an international presence to prevent the area from becoming the cause of big power involvement. By 1954 the situation had changed: North Vietnam had become strong and determined and had active communist bloc support in the UN. I heard that when, in the late 1960s, a confidential survey was made by the Johnson administration, only about twelve votes could be found to support a UN initiative in Vietnam. The UN did nothing about Vietnam partly because it lacked the tools, but fundamentally because it lacked the will.

In 1956, to continue the minuses, the Soviet aggression against Hungary could not be stopped. In 1968 Czechoslovakia could not be protected against a Soviet takeover. In both cases the only nation strong enough to have done so was the U.S., and we believed that our intervention would have involved an unconscionable risk. In 1971, the UN did not make a determined effort to persuade the government of Pakistan to cease its brutal behavior toward the East Pakistanis. It is true that the United Nations Charter forbids interference in a state's "internal affairs"—and the conduct of Pakistani officials in Pakistan, in one sense, was very "internal." But the UN can, without using force, intervene in a nation's internal affairs when it fears that developments there constitute a threat to the peace. This was not done with regard to Pakistan. Nor did the UN prevent—or try to prevent—India from invading East Pakistan.

Another defect in the UN is that voting does not correspond to the ability to carry out the things which are voted. The rapid decolonization of territories formerly under British, Belgian, and French rule has brought many small independent states into the UN, some with populations of less than one million and one—the Maldive Islands—with only about ninety thousand inhabitants in its 115 square miles. Today there are in the world some seventy other states or territories with

151

populations of less than one million, many of which may seek membership in the UN in the future. Two-thirds of the votes in the General Assembly are now cast by states which contribute altogether only 4.5 percent of the regular budget. Sixty-three members pay the minimum rate of only .04 percent of the regular budget. Yet many small states still have difficulty meeting their assessments and maintaining missions at UN headquarters adequate to permit significant participation in the UN's activities.

There is also an alarming tendency not to consider questions on their merits, but to vote as blocs.

The lateness in starting the meetings, the windiness of the oratory, the lack of germaneness, and the much too lengthy so-called debates all make a bad impression.

Finally, there can today in our UN of 132 members be little confidence that, even if a clear and unambiguous case of aggression came before the Security Council or General Assembly, a majority of the members would treat it as such and would come to the aid of the victim.

This should alarm us. Dag Hammarskjold, the secretary-general, commented to me shortly before the invasion of Egypt in 1956 that "if the United Nations fails vigorously and effectively to block such a use of force other than in self-defense, it will cease to be a respectable organization." He was using the word *respectable* in its literal sense as meaning "worthy of respect." To him the mainspring of the Charter were the words in Article I, Paragraph 1, which gave as one of the "purposes of the United Nations" the "suppression of acts of aggression."

His was an important opinion, for he was a brilliant man of great integrity and with an unusual understanding of people and their actions. To digress for a moment, his stamina when tensions were greatest was enormous. This enabled him to work around the clock. He had a marked ability to perceive shadings and distinctions, invisible to the ordinary man. When these shadings were expressed in writing it looked like hairsplitting to the uninitiated, but it is often by using words so as to make differing interpretations possible that bitter international disputes can get settled. My friendship with him began in 1954 when he made the long, hard trip to Peking and was successful in bringing about the release of our fifteen American flyers who were imprisoned in communist China. He wrote just as he was leaving:

30 December 1954

Dear Cabot,

At the moment of my departure I want to drop you a note to thank you for all of your co-operation in connection with the preparation for the mission. Your understanding of the numerous practical problems involved has been much appreciated.

I have appreciated particularly the role that you have played in attempting to reduce to a minimum general discussion regarding this matter and thereby producing a more favorable climate for the attainment of my objective.

I want to thank you also for your efforts in securing the Super Constellation for the first lap of my journey. As I approach the moment of my departure I appreciate it all the more as providing an opportunity for quiet reflection.

With very best wishes, I am

Very sincerely yours,
Dag

Hammarskjold's view that the UN only sanctions force when used in self-defense explains much of the criticism which has been made of the United Nations Charter and which springs from the belief that the Charter is concerned only with stopping war and ignores considerations of justice. These critics believe that the injustice which impels nations to commit the aggression should also be dealt with.

In truth, the Charter does not ignore considerations of justice. Indeed it allows for efforts to achieve justice, provided these efforts do not involve the use of force. Force can only be used in self-defense. In an organization devoted primarily to peace, must this not always be the rule?

The Charter is also criticized because it prohibits interference by the UN in internal questions. But the UN can deal with internal questions which endanger world peace, such as civil wars. Here too, however, it is not allowed to use force.

We forget that the words in the Charter calling for the suppression of acts of aggression—that is, self-defense—were put in because most of the founders of the UN—Roosevelt, Churchill, Truman, among others—had seen Kaiser William II bring about World War I. All had seen Hitler bring about World War II. They thus believed that if the Kaiser and Hitler had known in advance that the United States was committed to suppressing aggression, they would never have aggressed. Therefore, the UN Charter said that we should not allow little wars to turn into big ones. We should say instead that we will enter the little wars in self-defense when they are still little, thereby keeping them little. If we said in advance that we would do so, then maybe even the little wars would not happen. We should, according to the thought in 1945, have told the Kaiser in 1914 that if he violated Belgian neutrality, the United States would be there. We should have told Hitler that the same consequences would follow his entrance into the Rhineland in 1939. Of course in both instances the United States would have had to be ready for a possible show of force.

Such thinking led the U.S. and the UN to enter the fighting in Korea—not as an end in itself, but as a way to suppress an

154

act of aggression by North Korea, abetted by mainland China and the Soviet Union, which, if unchecked, would, it was believed, surely have threatened Japan, thus starting a very large war indeed which would probably also have eventually involved Europe. "History will cite Korea," says Richard Rovere, "as the proving ground of collective security, up to this time no more than a plausible theory. It will cite it as the turning point of the world struggle against communism and as the scene of a great victory for American arms, one the future will celebrate even though the present does not."

Is the UN fated either to be ridiculous because it does nothing or, if it effectively stops countries in pursuit of their individual concepts of justice, to incur their bitter hatred? The answer to this question is that we sometimes expect too much from the UN. Churchill, with his magnificent practicality, said that the UN was not designed to take us to heaven, but to prevent us from going to hell. In other words, in one very real sense we should not expect it to bring peace, but be very happy if it prevents war. The two are not the same. Spinoza says that "peace is not absence of war; it is a virtue, a state of mind, a disposition for benevolence, confidence, justice." To achieve this kind of peace requires profound changes in our way of looking at things and in the things we deem important —something clearly beyond the scope of the UN. We must not wait for these changes before trying to prevent war.

We have not waited. The world is already a better place than it would have been were there no UN, as my list of pluses shows. The view of the earth from space ships and from the moon shows, too, as nothing else could, that the earth's peoples are interdependent.

The members of the UN must therefore develop the will to bring about a rapid expansion of its effectiveness. It is up to the members. They cannot duck the responsibility. For there really is no alternative.

155

CHAPTER FIVE

☆ ☆ ☆ ☆ ☆ ☆ ☆ ☆ ☆ ☆

With Khrushchev in America

On August 22, 1959 the White House announced: "In response to an invitation from President Eisenhower, Nikita S. Khrushchev, Chairman of the Council of Ministers of the Union of Soviet Socialist Republics, will visit the United States from September 15th through September 27th. . . .

"The Honorable Henry Cabot Lodge, United States Ambassador to the United Nations and a member of the President's Cabinet, will accompany the Chairman on his travels within the United States as personal representative of the President." *

* I believe Major General Wilton B. ("Jerry") Persons, who replaced Sherman Adams as the assistant to the president, suggested me for this task. As the army's representative on Capitol Hill just before and during the war, his talent for explanation and persuasion was crucial in bringing about timely enactment of the Selective Service Act.

Thus began twelve extraordinary days with an extraordinary man.

First, however, before Chairman Khrushchev's arrival, I was stuffed full of information on every subject which he could conceivably raise. For two weeks I was a veritable walking encyclopedia.

On September 15, he and his party swooped down in a beautiful silver plane at Andrews Field, the large U.S. Air Force base near Washington. The president, the cabinet, and the press were all on hand, curious and hopeful about this unprecedented visit of a Soviet chief of government.* There were flurries of official greetings, speeches, reviewing of troops, and playing of national anthems. Chairman Khrushchev and President Eisenhower then walked under the crossed American and Soviet flags (Andrews Field was the only place where the two flags were crossed), entered the president's car, and the two of them drove to Blair House, the elegant, yellow federalist house on Pennsylvania Avenue where in 1861 General Scott had offered Robert E. Lee the command of the Union Army, and which is now used as the official residence for high-ranking visitors.

Chairman Khrushchev was just finishing lunch with his family when I was ushered in. I told him who I was, saying that it was a great honor to accompany him and that I hoped his trip would be successful. If there was anything he wanted to do differently or anything special he wanted to see, we would try to oblige.

Looking me up and down with a certain amusement, he said, "Before coming over here I read your speeches and after I read them I thought I would be scared of you, but now that I have been with you, talked with you, and seen what a nice man

* The Soviet "chief of state" is largely a ceremonial figure about whom the world hears little.

you are I don't feel scared any more." He was referring to our policy in the UN of giving as good as we got after Soviet attacks. Our Soviet visitor was obviously a diplomat, a politician, and a polite guest, with a marked sense of the ridiculous.

When I asked him whether Mrs. Khrushchev would like my wife to make any arrangements for her, he asked if I did not realize that in the USSR the women made their own decisions—and that, apparently, in the U.S.A. it was otherwise?

Several times during his stay—with a grin—he would remark, "Mr. Lodge, I want you to understand one thing: I have not come to the United States to learn anything about America. We know all we need to know about America and we learn it through our Marxist instruction." To which I invariably replied, "Thank you for telling me, Mr. Chairman. We will do our utmost to comply with your wishes."

Granting that any man who is the chief executive of the Soviet Union is impressive, Mr. Khrushchev was even more remarkable as a human being and would have made an imprint on those he met even without his mighty office. His eyes were clear and blue and could at various times be cold, kindly, or gay. He looked ebullient, as do those who sleep and eat well. His personal magnetism was immediately felt. Here was a natural politician—a man who, on entering a room full of strangers, would, after a few hours, have persuaded some, charmed and amused others, and frightened still more, so that by the end of the day he would have over 50 percent of their votes!

That afternoon, on our way down Constitution Avenue, we drove past the flaming sword of gold erected as a memorial to the Third Division. He asked what it was. When I told him, he commented, "That monument is very warlike. In my country there is nothing like that." He showed surprise, however, when I told him that the money for the monument was

159

raised by veterans of the Third Division, that the design was chosen by them, and that the government had nothing to do with it.

Later we passed the Jefferson Memorial and he discussed the phrase attributed to Jefferson that he would rather have a country with a free press and no government than a government with no free press. This, said Khrushchev, was doubtless a fine phrase at a time when the world was emerging from feudalism, but it didn't apply now because "you haven't got a free press in this country. You have a commercial press operated by individuals for profit who consult only their own interests. A free press is only free for rich people like Hearst who own newspapers. Things are much better in the Soviet Union where the press is run by the government for the benefit of everyday people."

As the car sped along, he pointed out a highway worker sweeping the road and remarked, "Now how can that man possibly influence any newspaper? Journalism should be educational—not a business."

He then switched the conversation to American politics—a subject which seemed to interest him deeply—and asked if a very rich man like Rockefeller could be elected president. I answered yes, if the people want him. If Rockefeller were president, Chairman Khrushchev continued, he would, when he left public office, have enough to live, on, adding, "In my country I haven't got money. So when I leave office I will be taken care of by the country." I explained that all our presidents, rich and poor, receive a pension from the government.

He was a good listener and gave the impression of being a man with an open mind—but on certain subjects only. He often picked up details of former conversations and used them in later discussions.

160

The next day, on the train going to New York, he noticed some dilapidated, wooden, two-story tenements and remarked that they had old houses in the Soviet Union, but did not build like that any more. I agreed that such houses were deplorable, but then asked him to look out the left-hand side of the train where there were new houses. He said this was fair, adding, "We have a lot more bad housing than you have," and "I have not come here to look at bad things, of which we have enough at home."

He then told me that the night before his advisers had told him to beware of me as I would want to twist him around my little finger, adding that I would show him only the good things, hoping the bad would go unnoticed. He had answered that he did not want to see anything that I did not want to show him.

He then spoke of my arguments with the Soviets in the UN, saying, "Go in and give the Russian diplomats Hell. Beat them up; it is good for them; they will get wiser that way." Gromyko, who then was heard for the first time, said, "I disagree." Khrushchev responded, "You see! The man speaks up for himself."

The schedule was unbelievably full. Every minute was taken, with scant opportunities to rest or relax. Like many of his party, Chairman Khrushchev seemed to feel the heat.

After spending September 17 in New York, we set out on the morning of the eighteenth to visit President Roosevelt's grave at Hyde Park. Chairman Khrushchev asked to visit Harlem and it had been decided to stop there on the way back from Hyde Park. While at Hyde Park, the chairman and Mrs. Roosevelt had such a long and cordial conversation that the whole trip fell behind schedule. The chairman was expected to address the General Assembly of the UN and wanted to go to his hotel to put on a dark suit for the occasion. This meant that he had to go directly there, omitting the Harlem tour—as he would already be a little late.

When I told him this, Ambassador Mikhail A. Menshikov, a troublemaker as far as I was concerned, immediately exclaimed in a bitter tone, "Notice how the Americans want to prevent you from going to Harlem. This is because they have something to hide." I replied that we had nothing to hide and that he would see Harlem before he left New York, if it was the last thing I did. Out of the tail of my eye I could see that Chairman Khrushchev greatly enjoyed this rather crude exchange between Ambassador Menshikov and me.

The next morning, instead of leaving the Waldorf Astoria at 8:00 A.M. as had been planned, we left at 7:00 (with breakfast at 6:00) so that we could drive through Harlem, which at that hour was quite deserted. It was a bright, sunny summer day and the neighborhood seemed less congested than usual. Chairman Khrushchev in a rather jovial and expansive tone noted, "Well, this isn't bad. We have a lot of areas just like this in the Soviet Union." Having been carefully briefed on our hopes rather than on reality, I responded, "Well, bad or not, these buildings are all coming down very soon!"

Once at Kennedy Airport, we boarded a special plane which the president had put at the chairman's disposal to fly us to Los Angeles. His wife, his two daughters, and his son-in-law, Alexis Adzubei, were with him in a large private cabin at the front of the plane. At noon, he invited me to join him for a brandy, complete with toasts to peace. After draining the glass we turned it upside down, each over his own head. This became a frequent event—a symbol of our good relations—and, although hardly my usual routine, I survived rather pleasantly.

The official schedule for our stay in Los Angeles one day showed some free time after lunch, which was to be at the Twentieth Century Fox cafeteria. I telephoned from the plane to the chief of police of Los Angeles and asked him whether he had any suggestions of interesting things to do in the afternoon. He said that we could visit a supermarket or a housing project or else go to Disneyland. I said I would consult the chairman and then call back. When I told the Khrushchev party about this, the young ladies expressed a desire to see Disneyland, to which their father agreed.

In my second conversation with the chief of police I told him that the chairman and his party preferred to go to Disneyland and then added, "Now Chief, are you sure that you can guarantee security on a trip to Disneyland, because we will not go anywhere where you do not guarantee security." He replied that he could.

We arrived in Los Angeles in a smoldering, Saharalike heat. As the whole party got into the automobiles, a youth threw a tomato which may have been aimed at Chairman Khrushchev, but which missed him and hit the vehicle in which the chief of police was driving. We arrived at the cafeteria at Twentieth Century Fox—a very long and narrow hall. Huge floodlights on one side of the room illuminated the head table where the lunch was being presented on live television. Many well-known actors and actresses were there. My inexpert eye detected Marilyn Monroe, David Niven, and Maurice Chevalier, to name only a few. I was seated about six places from Chairman Khrushchev and, sitting next to me, was my colleague, Ambassador Menshikov. The heat from the floodlights, added to the weather and the low ceiling, made the place almost unbearable.

During lunch the chief of police suddenly appeared behind me. His face looked gray and he appeared under great tension. He said, "I want you as the representative of the president to know that I will not be responsible for Chairman Khrushchev's

163

safety if we go to Disneyland." I replied, "Very well, Chief. If you will not be responsible for his safety, we do not go and we will do something else. I do not want to go anywhere where the police will not take responsibility for Chairman Khrushchev's safety."

Ambassador Menshikov, next to me, heard this conversation. He immediately arose and walked over to where the chairman was sitting at the center of the head table and told him that I had canceled the trip to Disneyland. Back came a message from the chairman which read, "I understand you have canceled the trip to Disneyland. I am most displeased."

In the meantime, I had received grateful words from General Zakharov, the Soviet chief of security. So I sent back a message, "General [Nikolay S.] Zakharov approves my decision not to go to Disneyland."

Back came another message, "General Zakharov is one man, I am another man!"

From lunch we went to one of the studios where the film *Can Can* was being produced and, of course, what was shown to the chairman were the girls doing the cancan, exposing plenty of bare thighs and black garters—which gave him a great opportunity later on to talk about American decadence and the impropriety of causing young girls thus to expose their bodies.

After the dance was over, I noticed one of the Hollywood photographers trying to get two of the girls who were being photographed on either side of Mr. Khrushchev to lift their skirts. I also noted several of Mr. Khrushchev's Soviet companions, notably Georgiy A. Zhukov, observing the American photographer trying to promote what they obviously thought would be a sexy picture not helpful to their boss. But the girls, without any prompting from anybody, declined. When President Eisenhower heard about this, he said that he wished that he could have had the names of the two girls as he would have written each one of them a letter of thanks.

After *Can Can* we started on a tour of Los Angeles, as the trip to Disneyland had been canceled. Chairman Khrushchev and I got into the inevitable closed, armored Cadillac. As we inched slowly through the traffic, I noticed an obviously agitated woman dressed in black, with a big black hat, standing on the street corner waving a black flag with one hand. In her other hand she held a sign on which were printed the words, "Death to Khrushchev, the butcher of Hungary."

Chairman Khrushchev noticed the woman too and asked what she signified. I said, "Well, Mr. Chairman, this is a woman who does not agree with certain aspects of your foreign policy."

Khrushchev said angrily, "Well, if Eisenhower wanted to have me insulted, why did he invite me to come to the United States in the first place?"

I responded, "Do I understand that you think that President Eisenhower invited you to come to the United States and then arranged to have this woman stand on this street corner in Los Angeles so as to insult you?"

Chairman Khrushchev replied, "Well, in the Soviet Union she wouldn't be there unless I had given the order." He seemed indignant.

He then told a representative of city hall who had joined us that he was extremely well informed about the United States through his intelligence service. "The Soviet Union," he said, "has even got money from the United States for its intelligence work." Some of the agents who had been sent by the United States to the Soviet Union had, he said, been caught and the Soviet intelligence service had kept sending reports to Allen Dulles, the chief of our Central Intelligence Agency, in their names with occasional requests for additional funds.

165

Those funds had been received and used for Soviet intelligence operations. There had also been agents who defected to the Soviet Union who had been sent back to the United States as Soviet double agents. He said he knew about a highly confidential message from President Eisenhower to Mr. Nehru, then prime minister of India, which the president had written in connection with the Chinese-Indian border dispute. I probably didn't know about it, Chairman Khrushchev said, "but if you wished, I could supply you with a copy," which he never did. He said he read much of the "stuff" put out by Dulles, but he would rather read good novels.

The interminable afternoon dragged on.

We visited a supermarket, which provided many opportunities for photographs. The State Department had been unable to arrange a pool of a few photographers and a few journalists to represent the media as a whole, so we were constantly in danger of being literally overrun by photographers and reporters—all four hundred of them. I remember one photographer in particular dashing along the counter up to his ankles in spam, cheese, sliced turkey, and other foods in order to get ahead of Chairman Khrushchev and turn around to get a picture of him wading through the groceries.

Finally, we got to the hotel where a stand-up cocktail party lasting an hour was held before the civic dinner. Before entering the hotel we stopped long enough to permit Ambassadorr Menshikov to point out the smog hovering over the city. Knowing that the mayor was going to speak at the banquet, I asked him if he would show me a copy of his speech, which he did. The speech contained the usual attack on Chairman Khrushchev because of his having once said to the United States, "we will bury you." This had been thrown at him at the National Press Club in Washington a few days before and Chairman Khrushchev had made it clear that he had not meant

166

that they would bury us by force of arms, but, figuratively, because of the superiority of the communist system. To repeat this attack twice in forty-eight hours would have been definitely discourteous. Chairman Khrushchev would unquestionably think that the U.S. government had instigated it. I, therefore, requested the mayor not to make this attack. The mayor declined, saying that the speech was written and distributed and he was not going to change it. He felt sure that I was wrong.

The mayor's speech came late in the evening—around 11:00 P.M. local time (2:00 A.M. in New York) and appeared to enrage Chairman Khrushchev. He announced that he had not come to America to be insulted, that he was calling for his plane, and spoke about flying to Vladivostok the next day.

It was 2:00 A.M. local time when I reached my room—twenty-four hours after arising in New York. One of my daily chores was to dictate a telegram to the State Department at the end of each day reporting on what had happened and also reporting on matters which I had been instructed to take up with Chairman Khrushchev, if there was an opportunity. These might either be hardship cases—old people in the Soviet Union who wished to join their children in the U.S.—or the plight of Jews in the Soviet Union. He was usually helpful on the first category and negative on the second.

As I was dictating the telegram to a secretary, the telephone rang. It was Andrei Gromyko, saying he wished to see me immediately. In a moment he was there and, as he sat down and crossed his legs, I noticed that, in spite of the heat, he wore long underdrawers over which his socks were pulled. Having known him for many years, I was aware that he suffered from hay fever and was sure that the heat and smog were making him uncomfortable. I also believed that, unlike Ambassador Menshikov, he wanted the trip to be a success. He began, "I

167

have come to make an official protest at the discourtesy shown to Chairman Khrushchev today."

When asked what the discourtesy was, he referred to the woman who had been standing on the street corner.

I answered, "Mr. Minister, you have been ambassador in Washington and you understand our system of government. You know very well that it is inconceivable that President Eisenhower would invite Chairman Khrushchev to come to this country and then arrange to have this woman stand on the sidewalk in Los Angeles. How can I accept this protest?"

Clearly the Khrushchev visit to America was becoming a horrible failure. Chairman Khrushchev had said to me repeatedly, "You Americans are keeping me in house arrest." He resented being in closed limousines, cut off from the crowd. If the trip was a failure for him, then it was a failure for the United States. The schedule therefore had to be changed. He had to have more time to himself. He should be transported in open cars, thus getting him closer to the people. A telephone call to the chief of police of San Francisco brought assurance that there would be open cars there.

The next day the whole party took the Southern Pacific air-conditioned train from Los Angeles to San Francisco. Chairman Khrushchev was more cheerful then he had been the night before and had apparently dropped the idea of flying to Vladivostok. The schedule had been changed, I told him. We were going to run things so that he would see more people, adding, "Of course, you understand, Mr. Chairman, that some enthusiastic friend may throw a bunch of flowers at you and you may get scratched." He smiled and said, "I know. I have had that happen to me in the Soviet Union."

"We have decided to manage the trip as though you were a presidential candidate," I said. "We will do some whistle stops." I explained that a whistle stop meant that the train stops for a moment or two, during which time he would have a chance to get out; kiss a few babies, if he felt like it; and say a few words to the crowd. Then the whistle would blow and off he would go again. He seemed to like the idea.

As the train stood in the station, demonstrators came by with hostile signs which he had his interpreter translate for him. His view had so changed since the previous day that he remarked, "Poor Eisenhower! I am just now beginning to understand what his problems are."

The first stop was in Santa Barbara—a beautiful place which had attracted many solvent Boston friends. In that morning's papers was an announcement by President Eisenhower, who was obviously concerned at the turn the Khrushchev trip was taking, urging Americans to be polite to our guest, and remarking that politeness to a guest does not require one to agree with all his opinions.

Thus, when the train pulled into Santa Barbara, there was a large and friendly crowd at the station. It was a beautiful, hot day and the men were dressed in short-sleeved shirts and waved American flags. As I stepped off the train several Bostonians in the crowd yelled, "Hi! Cabot!" I presented Chairman Khrushchev to the assembled company and he got a round of applause. He saw a pretty little girl in the front row, picked her up, and gave her a big kiss. He shook hands with the ladies and bowed low. He had some red hammer and sickle pins stuck in the lapel of his coat. He took them out and pinned them on several of the men. This produced even more applause. In the midst of this enthusiastic atmosphere the whistle blew. "Please mount up, Mr. Chairman," said the conductor. The crowd gave him a thunderous farewell. He got on board. The train moved out and, as we stood there in the vestibule, he turned to me, "Now, Lodge, I want you to notice one thing. The plain people of America like me. It's just those bastards around Eisenhower that don't."

An incident of a different kind took place when the train stopped at San Luis Obispo. As the representative of the president, it was my duty to be at Chairman Khrushchev's side. My identity was obviously not known to some of the Soviet secret service men whom Chairman Khrushchev had brought with him. In particular, there was a young muscular man who kept mistaking me for a journalist or a photographer and had twice "lifted me out"—coming at me from behind, clutching me in a strong embrace, and carrying me away. This definitely interfered with my performance of duty and it was beginning to annoy me. The young man spoke no English and I had been too busy to talk to him through an interpreter. In the railroad station in San Luis Obispo I saw him coming at me for the third time. Before he had a chance to move me, I grabbed him and pushed him into a corner of the railroad station and muttered, "Don't ever lay a hand on me again."

General Zakarov, pushing his way through the crowd, came up to apologize, and a few minutes later, when I saw Khrushchev, he spread out his arms wide and said with an enormous grin on his face, "I hear you have been beating up one of my guards." He was obviously delighted and his attitude toward me became much friendlier and remained so for the rest of the trip.

Most of the four hundred journalists with us had hardly more than seen the chairman. All they had been able to do so far was to be part of a mob. It was therefore decided that Chairman Khrushchev would walk through the train so that at least every journalist there could say truthfully that he had met him.

Had I known what a long and strenuous walk this was going to be, I might not have undertaken it. Chairman Khrushchev reveled in it, however, and took advantage of all questions to put out his favorite line of talk, addressing himself particularly to the corruption and decadence of Hollywood.

He talked at great length about his stay in Los Angeles, expressing his annoyance about the treatment he had received there and, in particular, about the fact that no one from the city had been on hand at the railroad station to say good-by to him or to ask him to say a few words to the population of Los Angeles, even though microphones had been set up on the platform. I apologized and hoped Chairman Khrushchev would understand that we had no centralized power in our country as in Europe and that the actions of local officials could not be controlled.

He also told Ambassador Llewellyn Thompson, our brilliant representative in Moscow, that he could not understand how such good and hard-working people as the Americans could patronize such entertainment as that which he had seen in Hollywood. The only reason for that, he thought, might be the extreme abundance of wealth in the United States which made the people look for such entertainment. He thought the attempt of a reporter to make a dancer lift her skirt while she was being photographed with him was in very poor taste.

Finally it was time for lunch, with our usual shot of brandy beforehand. Beer and wine were also served. As we left the diner we went through a special car in which there was a large stateroom. The door was slightly open, the bed invitingly turned down. As we went by I showed him the room and asked him if he would not like to take a nap. He said he would and did—for a good two hours. This made the rest of the day run on well-oiled wheels.

When we reached San Francisco early in the evening, he went immediately to a meeting with representatives of American labor where he was treated with roughness and hostility—

171

in contrast to the reception in Santa Barbara in the morning. But by that time the Khrushchev party was on the track and nothing bothered him any more.

Here are a few excerpts from his fantastic exchanges with labor leaders Walter P. Reuther and James B. Carey:

KHRUSHCHEV: The United States exploits the wealth of other countries, underdeveloped countries, for profits. England and France do the same. They exploit the wealth of countries that need aid. We do not exploit any country—we only engage in trade.

REUTHER: You exploit the workers of East Germany.

KHRUSHCHEV: Where did you dream that up?

REUTHER: If you don't exploit them, why should three million of them cross the border into West Germany?

KHRUSHCHEV: You are hopelessly sick with capitalist fever.
[Several voices interchanging across table.]

REUTHER: The workers in West Germany are free . . .

KHRUSHCHEV: We are free, too.

REUTHER: Do you have credentials to speak for the workers of the world?

KHRUSHCHEV: Do you have credentials to poke your nose into East Germany?

CAREY: This is part of our difficulty: the fear of the chairman that the United States actually wants to dominate the world.

KHRUSHCHEV: Not just wants—striving!

CAREY: And the other way around, there is the fear in the United States, based on much evidence, that the Soviet Union wants to dominate the world.

KHRUSHCHEV: The Soviet ruble does not kowtow to the American dollar. [At this point Khrushchev raised his voice loudly and vehemently.] You have been spoiled by everyone bowing down, by everyone cringing and crawling.

172

What a contrast with Soviet-American exchanges today! The authorities in San Francisco, notably the mayor and chief of police, showed that they knew how to receive their guest. Everything went perfectly, and at the end of a sunset drive over the San Francisco hills, Khrushchev turned to me and said, "This city has quite bewitched me," adding with dumbfounding frankness, "it would take us two and a half times as long to build what San Francisco represents as we say that it would."

On another occasion he had spoken of communism with such fervor that it prompted me to ask whether, for him, it was not in truth a religion—or a cult. To which he replied heatedly, "That's how you put it. Actually it's the science of history." One could not help thinking of Henry Adams's prolonged search for a science of history. I also learned from his evident annoyance that this was not a suitable topic for casual conversation.

He admired the San Francisco Bay Bridge and our highway construction in general, noting that under our capitalistic system the practice of collecting tolls from those who use bridges and highways was sound and rational, but that it was not possible in the Soviet Union where there was no private property, evidently thinking that American bridges were privately owned.

I asked whether it was not true that in the Soviet Union the people were allowed to own homes and leave them to their children in their will. Did this indicate that even in the Soviet Union there was private property?

Chairman Khrushchev answered that there was a difference between private property and personal property. Things like automobiles, homes, clothing, and the like were considered to be personal property. It was the means of production which belonged to the entire people and that couldn't be held by individual citizens.

At a meeting of the International Longshoremen's Association he took off his cap and put it on the head of one of the workers, much to everybody's amusement. He liked to give things away—hammer and sickle pins to the crowd in Santa Barbara, a cap to the Longshoremen's Association, a Russian-made wristwatch at the Mesta Steel Works in Pittsburgh. He sent one of his assistants out to buy him a hat in San Francisco and I happened to be standing in his suite at the hotel when the hat was delivered to him. He put it on and said he liked it very much and thought it was a nice hat. Immediately Ambassador Menshikov said it was typically cheap, shoddy American manufacture.

He was a natural rough and tumble debater and loved to interrupt whoever happened to be speaking. He did not, however, enjoy being interrupted himself. During our twelve days together he tried to draw me out about my life and, upon learning that I had been in the army reserve, asked me what my rank was. I said I had been made a major general. He said that he had ended up as a lieutenant general which, he pointed out, meant that he outranked me. I said that this was indeed true: He outranked me in more ways than one and I would always try to respect his rank.

On our way to the airport he suggested building a tunnel under San Francisco Bay to provide a rapid public transportation system to downtown San Francisco. On second thought, he added, a bridge might be cheaper. He was surprised to learn from the mayor that the estimates for a tunnel were cheaper than those for a bridge.

Mr. Khrushchev then referred to an idea advanced by Stalin, who, he said, "had had many silly ideas," to build a railroad to Sakhalin with a tunnel under the Tatar Strait in eastern Siberia. Stalin had argued that a tunnel would be better from a military point of view because the Americans would not see it from the air and thus could not destroy it." To this Khrushchev had replied that the Americans could see the approaches to the tunnel and thus hit its entrances. Stalin then became very angry at Khrushchv. After Stalin's death the whole plan was scrapped, although some preliminary work had been done.

Like everything on the trip, we visited Iowa because Chairman Khrushchev wanted to do so. He had a personal friend there; the distinguished farmer, Roswell Garst of Coon Rapids, Iowa. He had had many conversations and much correspondence with him concerning corn, the feeding of animals, and other agricultural matters. Arriving at Des Moines in the evening, Chairman Khrushchev was told by Mr. Garst, "Now, Khrushchev, tomorrow you'll have the kind of a day you haven't had yet. You'll be out on my farm all alone with me. There will be no press and nobody to bother us."

In the morning Chairman Khrushchev, Mr. Garst, and I set forth from Des Moines into the beautiful, lush green Iowa countryside. Much to Mr. Garst's astonishment, he found, on apporaching his farm, that men and women in quantities suggestive of an armored division were trampling his fields. Journalists of the written word, photographers, electronic reporters with their cumbersome equipment were all on hand. Mr. Garst flew into a rage and ordered several of his young men who were on horseback to charge the representatives of the media. He directed the operator of a huge piece of farm machinery to run the interlopers down. Seeing one distinguished-looking man with glasses and a moustache who did not obey his order to depart, Mr. Garst administered a vigorous kick to the gentleman's rear end, slipped so that both his feet went out from under him, and impaled himself on a cornstalk. This particular

175

THE STORM HAS MANY EYES

interloper turned out to be none other than Harrison Salisbury of the New York *Times*. Chairman Khrushchev was overcome with laughter.

It was a long day outdoors. Chairman Khrushchev took great amusement in cautioning me, the capitalist, about stepping in the manure, saying that it is not the manure that you get on your feet that will cause you trouble in life, but the manure that is in your soul or in your heart. As we marched across the fields, through the enclosures, and into the barns, the gentlemen of the press followed close behind, always pushing so that they might hear what was being said. At the head of this unusual procession was Chairman Khrushchev talking to Farmer Garst. In between was Alexander Akalovsky, the American interpreter, or Viktor M. Sukhodrov, the Russian interpreter. I was immediatly behind the chairman (he being very short and I very tall), holding hands with our security men, digging in our heels, and leaning back so as to prevent the crowd in back of us from overrunning Chairman Khrushchev. Necessity being the mother of invention, I obtained an electric megaphone for one of the Secret Service men to hold on his shoulder pointing backward. This was connected to a microphone which the interpreter held so that it would pick up whatever he or Chairman Khrushchev or Farmer Garst said and would be boomed out to the journalists; the pressure then diminished.

Looking back over his American journey, it was clear that Khrushchev had seen and learned a great deal. He was most observant, intelligent, and perspicacious. I had the feeling that he looked at us quite differently on September 27 than he had on September 15. On his arrival word had leaked out from his party that he had come to the United States to make propaganda against us. Yet he only criticized the U.S. once—regarding Hollywood. In his own way he had wooed the United States and said nothing that would anger the average

Senator Lodge speaks in Florida, 1961.   —G. *Tony Rura*

A 1960 campaign photo in New York City. Front Row: Mrs. Richard Nixon, President Dwight Eisenhower. With Vice-President Nixon, the author, and Emily Sears Lodge.

—Toni Frissell

At a government farm in Tashkent, the Soviet Union, 1960.

During his 1960 trip, the author had just bought bread and honey at Samarkand market when Uzbek man offered to shake hands.

At the Samarkand Market, a woman behind honey counter said, "All right now, young man, what do you want?" Aide Peter Thacher, Emily Sears Lodge, and Toumanov can be seen in crowd.

—Life *photo by Carl Mydans*

Saigon, 1964. Dedication of monument to memory of President John Kennedy. The author is shaking hands with General Nguyen Khanh, then prime minister of Vietnam.

Vietnam, 1963. Ambassador Lodge with President Ngo Dinh Diem (who was dead a week later). —*USIS, Press Section*

The author is sworn in for second time as United States ambassador to Vietnam, 1965. Those present include: President Lyndon Johnson, Secretary of State Dean Rusk, Under Secretary of State Nicholas Katzenbach, Senator Leverett Saltonstall (R-Mass.), Senator Bourke Hickenlooper (R-Iowa), Vice-President Hubert Humphrey, Emily Sears Lodge, Secretary of Treasury Henry H. Fowler, General Maxwell D. Taylor, Secretary of Defense Robert McNamara.

After Rose Garden swearing in ceremony, the president tells a joke in the oval office.

Danang, 1966. A visit to the Marines with Colonel George Jacobson, U.S. Mission coordinator, and Lieutenant General L. W. Walt.

—U.S. Marine Corp photograph

Back from Vietnam for consultation in 1966, the author meets with Secretary Dean Rusk, Secretary Robert McNamara, President Lyndon Johnson.

← Author returns to Washington, September 1967, with his report on Vietnamese elections. Those present include: Mayor Joseph Barr, Governor Richard Hughes, Senator Bourke Hickenlooper, President Lyndon Johnson, Vice-President Hubert Humphrey, Secretary Orville Freeman, Ambassador Arthur Goldberg, Secretary Dean Rusk, Secretary Robert McNamara, Secretary John Gardner, the author.

Bonn, 1968. The author with Leonard Bernstein and J. Robert Schaetzel, U.S. ambassador to the European Common Market.

New York City, May 24, 1972. Mrs. Dwight D. Eisenhower, the author.
—U.S. Navy photograph

Bonn, 1969. The author with Willy Brandt (then foreign minister).
—*J. H. Darchinger IFJ*

Rome, 1971. Pope Paul VI and the author. —*Felici*

President Nixon and the author back from Rome, 1971.

American. America, in its own way, had responded.

He had been impressed by the roads, automobiles, factories, farms, housing projects, drive-ins, the private planes owned by farmers in Iowa and the healthy, well-dressed appearance of the people. San Francisco, to him, was a great example of the achievements of capitalism: It made him "slightly envious." He had communism in his head, he said, but he had San Francisco in his heart—spectacular for the head of the Soviet Union to say at that time. He would comment, "You slaves of capitalism live well." He obviously believed that we had a way of life worth defending and that our "dynamic economy" was working.

He was worried about a slide to war. Maybe his visit opened a new relationship in which the value of talking was to become more appreciated. I have often asked myself, Where would we be if Khrushchev had not been asked to come? Surely we would be the worse for not having had him. There was a time when the Soviet line at the United Nations was that World War III would ruin us, but that they would not be hurt. Khrushchev's line, however, was, "Only a mad man would think of war." He clearly thought World War III would destroy us all. To prove his point that we could be different without fighting about it, he would often say, "Do you like beef? I like borsch. Very well, you eat your beef and I'll eat my borsch."

One American Soviet expert told me that what Khrushchev had seen on his American tour had basically affected his whole outlook and had made him realize the inadequacies of the standard Moscow line. Had his colleagues in the Politburo on his return sensed that he was no longer on the same wave length with them? In faraway Peking had Chou En Lai sensed it too? Did this lead to his retirement? Perhaps this is the price which must be paid for evolution in the thinking of great nations.

On his last day in Washington, he had, at a lunch, referred to me as *"moi brat"* which, I was told, means "my brother." He gave me a number of presents: a set of Soviet phonograph records, a black lacquer box with a picture of the Kremlin on the cover, a shotgun, and a large yellow and gold china vase almost two feet tall.

He also sent me from Moscow a book in Russian with an English translation, entitled *Krushchev in America* which contained the chairman's speeches—complete with numerous insertions in italics and in parentheses, "(applause)" or "(animation)" or "(laughter)." The words "(stormy, prolonged applause. All rise)" came after the closing lines of his homecoming speech in Moscow: "Long live friendship among the peoples of the world!"

In the book he also expressed thanks to all those who helped on his American tour and added, "I would like to thank them all, and especially Mr. Lodge. He did his best to create the necessary conditions for us on our tour and to acquaint us with the life of the great American people. (applause)

"I remarked in jest to Mr. Lodge that if he, a representative of the capitalist world, and I, a representative of the working class and the Communist party of the Soviet Union, were to be cast away on a desert island, we would probably find a common language and would be able to coexist peacefully. (animation, prolonged applause)"

On our last automobile ride he turned to me with a grin and said, "I want you to know that I have learned nothing new about America." To which I replied that I was relieved to hear this because I had tried to organize matters so that he would learn nothing.

In December from Moscow came a letter in Russian enclosed in a cardboard folder on which was embossed the seal of the Soviet Union. The following English translation was enclosed:

178

30 ноября 1959 года.

Уважаемый господин Лодж, уважаемый генерал-майор!

Имейте в виду, что это письмо пишет Вам генерал-лейтенант. Поэтому Вам, как генерал-майору, надлежит читать его стоя в положении по команде „смирно", как говорят военные.

Когда я был в Соединенных Штатах Америки, судьба свела нас с Вами. Вы сопровождали меня в поездке по стране и многое сделали для того, чтобы эта поездка была приятной и полезной. Вы были моим „мучителем" и „хранителем", Вы были оратором на многих собраниях и вместе с тем слушателем моих речей. Поэтому позвольте преподнести Вам экземпляр книги, изданной в Москве, в которой опубликованы материалы, связанные с моей поездкой в Соединенные Штаты Америки, в том числе и Ваши выступления.

Прошу передать от меня лично, а также от моей супруги и семьи сердечный привет Вашей супруге, которая также имела немало хлопот, путешествуя с нами по вашей стране.

С уважением   *Н.Хрущев*   Н.ХРУЩЕВ

Г-ну Генри Кэботу Лоджу,
гор.Нью-Йорк, США.

Dear Mr. Lodge, Dear Major General!

Bear in mind that a Lieutenant General is writing you this letter. Therefore, it is up to you as a Major General to read it standing at "attention" as the military say.

When I was in the United States fate brought us together. You accompanied me on my trip around the country and did a great deal in order that the trip would be pleasant and fruitful. You were my "tormentor" and "protector." You were a speaker at many gatherings as well as a listener of my speeches. Permit me therefore to present you with a copy of a book published in Moscow in which are given various items connected with my trip in the United States of America, including your speeches.

Please convey for me personally as well as from my wife and family heartfelt greetings to your wife who also had a great number of cares as she travelled with us around your country.

Sincerely,
N. Khrushchev

CHAPTER SIX

☆ ☆ ☆ ☆ ☆ ☆ ☆ ☆ ☆ ☆

Other Campaigns

In the late spring of 1960, Richard Nixon told me that it looked as though I should be the Republican nominee for vice-president. He asked me what my attitude would be should that happen.

I thanked him for the honor, adding that if I seemed suitable for vice-president, I would accept, believing that a man whose life has been spent in government should accept a party nomination for president or vice-president, barring some overriding personal reason.

A few weeks later the Republican Convention met in Chicago and at 3:00 A.M. I received a telephone call from Richard Nixon saying that he had attended a meeting of leading Republicans and that they all agreed that I should be the nominee for vice-president.

Never having thought of myself presidentially or vice-presidentially, I tried to figure out why I had been chosen. I think Dewey put his finger on it when he said that I had become very well known because TV coverage of the UN had been so extensive. Senator Bourke B. Hickenlooper of Iowa also said to me, "Cabot, I never thought I'd live to see the day when the people of Iowa favored someone like you for vice-president. You don't know anything about agriculture. Yet, the fact is that you are the one they want."

This was expressed in another way in the *Saturday Evening Post* by Clay Blair: "He is probably the most widely known, most talked about Vice Presidential candidate since Theodore Roosevelt ran with McKinley in 1900. He is instantly recognized everywhere, and if some political polls and pundits are to be believed, he generates more 'enthusiasm' than either Kennedy or Nixon. Second, Lodge, a former Senator considered politically dead in 1952, made his comeback entirely by means of a device of the electronic age. As United States Ambassador to the United Nations during the Eisenhower administration, Lodge became a big national figure simply by repeated display on television." *

And so I was pitchforked into a national campaign for vice-president. I had been out of politics since January 1953, having, on coming to the United Nations, resolved not to run for

* In *The Making of the President: 1960* (New York: Atheneum, 1961), pp. 206, 207, Theodore H. White says, "There ensued then the choice of a Vice President, performed in a closely guarded room in the Blackstone Hotel to which Nixon had summoned thirty-six Republican leaders in the small hours of Thursday morning, July 28th. . . . Nixon had tentatively chosen Henry Cabot Lodge as his running mate months before . . . but he now gave every man a chance to speak. . . .

"Nixon declared, 'If you ever let them [the Democrats] campaign only on domestic issues, they'll beat us—our only hope is to keep it on foreign policy.'

"Twenty of those present agreed with him that Henry Cabot Lodge was the best man to lift America's imagination to the problems of foreign policy, and since this was already Mr. Nixon's prior decision, so it was to be."

184

elective office again. Therefore, on the day of the vice-presidential nomination, I literally had no campaign staff at all. The able men and women who had worked with me in New York at the UN were all U.S. government civil servants and were, of course, precluded from taking any part in politics. I did not even know what their political affiliations were. Thus, as vice-presidential candidate, I had to form a staff from scratch.

My old friend Cammann Newberry, who had been my assistant in the Senate, stepped into the breach and in a very short time he had, with help from Richard Nixon, formed an excellent staff. How he did it and how it was possible for a group of men and women hastily assembled at the last minute to conduct such a professional campaign remains a mystery.

It is said that in a campaign for president or vice-president everything that can happen to upset one's equanimity happens. The trick is to have enough equanimity left for the last ten days and then fall across the finish line. Consider a typical day:

It would start—when not having an early breakfast with a big shot—by arising before sunrise in the presidential suite of a hotel in which the bed was usually too short and the room was usually right over the front door so that the usual lullaby was the backings and fillings of taxicabs with illuminations from a sign bearing the hotel's name flashing on and off during the night.

Leaving the hotel, I would indulge in a frantic search for votes, going to the nearest factory and standing at the gate to shake hands with men and women on their way to work. Then to the airport and a flight to some other city where, sitting atop the seat back of an open car, I would wave at the crowds—if there were any. At about 11:00 A.M. my wife would hand me a sardine sandwich which I held in my left hand while waving at the crowd enthusiastically with my

185

right. That would most of the time be lunch. Then would come a question and answer session at some college. Once, on leaving the college after one such session, one of my most assiduous helpers slammed the door of the car, catching my fingers in it. This required a stop at the hospital and had the great merit of getting me on the front page all over the country—a hard thing for a candidate for vice-president to do. What was a smashed finger compared to a headline!

Airplane rides often featured bad weather. In the plane it was usually necessary to write a press release for use that night. The plane would be bumping up and down in a thunderstorm while making an instrument approach. On arriving at about 6:00 P.M. I would sometimes be taken to the city hall and invited to step out onto a balcony looking out over a huge square filled with people. (Outdoor meetings always seemed to me more productive, as there was a hope that one could entice a few Democrats to listen who would under no condition enter a Republican rally.) My job was, first, to make the crowd laugh and, second, in the course of the speech to say something to make the crowd interrupt me with applause—more difficult than it sounds.

On leaving city hall for my hotel, I had ahead of me, at about 9:00 P.M., a major speech in the armory that night. This meant a forty minute talk with a prepared text. Yearnings for a shower, shave, and clean shirt—not to mention a scotch and soda—would sweep over me, but were rarely satisfied as, upon arrival at the hotel, a very important political leader would be waiting to see me. The state, it was explained, was very close, and thus the question of whether we carried that state, and thus the nation, could hinge on my seeing this man. So all the time before the big speech would be devoted to such key individuals.

After the speech, I would go back to my hotel room for the

process known to public speakers as "unwinding." Because the crowd reacts to the speaker and the speaker reacts to the crowd, unwinding must happen before the luxury of going to bed. This was, therefore, the time for visitors—editors, political leaders of all sorts, and prominent citizens; also local candidates to have their pictures taken; also an occasional drink.

One of the hair shirts which a national candidate wears comes from the efforts of local candidates to try to use a national campaign as an adjunct to their own campaigns. A competent advance man is indispensable—going ahead to make arrangements in every place where the candidate is to appear. One such advance man would visit the local TV station to adjust the lights—which can either make one look thirty-five or ninety-five years old. Another would see to it that the rostrum was at the right distance from the ground for someone as tall as I am—even if it meant that a shorter local candidate would have to stand on a soapbox to make his speech. The advance man would particularly try to protect me from having to go on all-night tours of political clubs and choice bars and grills—stops which can be absolutely crucial in a contest for alderman or the state legislature, but which are not always the best way for a vice-presidential candidate to campaign. My unwillingness to get involved in such local tactics sometimes caused local resentment and loose talk about my laying down on the job.

Sometimes we would have large and enthusiastic crowds, even in districts which never voted Republican. My resourceful representative to the media (newspapers and TV), Vincent P. O'Brien, told me that at least fifteen chiefs of police in as many different cities had said that the crowds which had come out to hear me were the greatest that they had seen during the campaign.

There was usually a laugh a day. One afternoon in New York, while driving through Queens, followed by my sound

187

truck covered with signs, we spied a bride, groom, and wedding party just coming out of church. When my indefatigable
tour director, Edward F. Terrar, who shepherded me all over
the United States, asked whether they would like to have
their picture taken with the Republican nominee for vice-
president, the bride gladly assented and so a picture was taken.
It must have been a felicitous wedding day for people in
Queens, because a few minutes later we came upon another
bridal couple emerging from another church. We immediately
dashed over for a picture, only to be told by the young bride
in no uncertain terms that she didn't want to have any politicians "lousing up" her wedding!

When election day finally came, Richard Nixon and I did
not squeak through. He sat up all night in California and I at
the Wardman Park Hotel in Washington. The results did not
become clear until almost sunrise. It had indeed been, as the
Duke of Wellington had said after Waterloo, "a damned close
run thing." But, after twenty-eight years in some sort of public
office, I was out.*

* In *Triumph and Tragedy* (Boston: Houghton Mifflin, 1953), pp.
674, 675, Winston Churchill describes the election of July 1945 when,
after years of inspired and brilliantly successful wartime leadership, he
was overwhelmingly defeated for re-election. When friends have been
defeated, I have cited it to them—always with comforting effect. It
reads,

> The latest view of the Conservative Central Office was that we
> should retain a substantial majority. I had not burdened myself
> unduly with the subject while occupied with the grave business
> of the Conference. On the whole I accepted the view of the
> party managers and went to bed in the belief that the British
> people would wish me to continue my work. My hope was that
> it would be possible to reconstitute the National Coalition Gov-
> ernment in the proportions of the House of Commons. Thus
> slumber. However, just before dawn I woke suddenly with a
> sharp stab of almost physical pain. A hitherto subconscious con-
> viction that we were beaten broke forth and dominated my

For some inexplicable reason on that sleepless day after the election—although I did not have a toothache—I felt the thing to do was to go to New York to have an annual inspection by my trusted friend and dentist, John P. Traugott. After a delightful session with no cavities, I caught the plane for Boston.

The telephone was ringing as I walked into my house in Beverly. I answered and found Henry R. Luce of *Time* and *Life* on the wire asking me to write an article for *Life*, on the United Nations. Nothing could have done me as much good. It was typical of his thoughtfulness and capacity for friendship. I shall always be grateful. The article for *Life* was duly produced—and, somewhat later, I had the good fortune to become a part-time consultant for Time Inc.

The last time I received any votes for public office was in the New Hampshire presidential primary of 1964. I was then ambassador to Vietnam, was not a candidate, and took no part whatever in the campaign. Yet I won. Professor Eugene Vasilew has written a lively and well-researched paper on this unusual political phenomenon in the April 1968 issue of *The Review of Politics* published by Notre Dame University. In the interests of objectivity—as the professor is clearly not a "Lodge man"—I will quote from it. He points out that

---

mind. All the pressure of great events, on and against which I had mentally so long maintained my "flying speed," would cease and I should fall. The power to shape the future would be denied me. The knowledge and experience I had gathered, the authority and goodwill I had gained in so many countries, would vanish. I was discontented at the prospect, and turned over at once to sleep again. I did not wake till nine o'clock, and when I went into the Map Room the first results had begun to come in. They were, as I now expected, unfavourable. By noon it was clear that the Socialists would have a majority. At luncheon my wife said to me, "It may well be a blessing in disguise." I replied, "At the moment it seems quite effectively disguised."

189

with very little money, no political power base, and not even a genuine candidate, the "Draft Lodge" movement brought off a stunning victory over the Goldwater and Rockefeller organizations which spent huge sums, between them controlled nearly all the sources of Republican power in New Hampshire, and had earnest candidates who tramped all over the snow-covered landscape shaking hands by the thousands and making speeches by the hundreds. How that victory was achieved is an instructive lesson in the vagaries of American presidential politics. It also happens to be a brilliant illustration of what has become known as the "public relations" campaign which, it turns out, works even better in primaries than in regular elections. Here then is the story of a political victory put together out of press releases and announcements, a couple of pieces of direct-mail advertising, a five-minute television film, and the mistakes of the other candidates. As for Lodge himself, he was 10,000 miles away in Saigon insisting he was not a candidate.

Former President Eisenhower made two statements in December 1963 which attracted attention to me. The first urged me to come and take part in Republican efforts to reach a consensus on a candidate. The second said that the Republicans could improve their chances of winning by choosing a moderate "common-sense" candidate with an impressive background in international affairs.

Professor Vasilew points out that "Lodge was, to put it generously, not popular with the Party leaders. In the first place, the conservatives held him responsible for stealing the nomination in 1952 from Senator Robert A. Taft, whom they idolized. Conservatives were also unsympathetic to his political views, which they associated with the Eastern wing of the Party and considered far too liberal. And finally, there was a widespread belief, not confined to conservatives, that as the vice-presidential candidate in 1960 he had let the party

190

down by campaigning without enthusiasm and on banker's hours."

Although the third criticism was, I thought, demonstrably untrue, undoubtedly some believed it.

These considerations faded into insignificance when two talented young political operators, David Goldberg and Paul Grindle, drove across the border into New Hampshire. These men, with the help of Sally Saltonstall and Carolyn Williams, all of whom had worked in my son George's campaign for the Senate against Edward M. Kennedy in 1962, made two huge mailings which constituted virtually the entire campaign effort.

There were three items in the first mailing: a brochure, which to cite Professor Vasilew again,

touched on all Lodge's noble qualities. . . . The Ambassador's selfless service was stressed: he had resigned from the United States Senate to serve in World War II; he had engineered Eisenhower's nomination and election in 1952; he had been for eight years Ambassador to the United Nations and was now Ambassador to South Vietnam. Lest the service of a Republican in a Democratic administration seem inconsistent with good Republicanism to some voters, President Kennedy was cited as follows: "Ambassador Lodge wanted to go to Saigon. If he were as careful as some politicians are, of course, he would not have wanted to go out there. He maybe would have liked to have some safe job, but he is energetic and he has strong feelings about the United States and, surprising as it seems, he put this ahead of his political career." . . . Under a picture of Lodge with the United Nations seal in the background, the caption read, in part: "Blunt, clear, unequivocal words and actions gave the free world leadership. Communist expansion was brought to a halt."

"It was natural," said the copy next to a picture of Lodge

191

with Eisenhower, "that this relationship should culminate in President Eisenhower's request that Ambassador Lodge return to the United States and seek the Republican nomination for President."

Professor Vasilew adds,

What made the Lodge campaign strategy so effective was its contrast with that of Goldwater and Rockefeller. While these two were challenging each other personally, and on the issues asking voters to decide whether it was wise to give field commanders control over nuclear weapons, admit Communist China to the United Nations, give federal aid to education, and other such difficult and controversial matters, the Lodge campaign was full of encomium for Lodge, but opprobrium for no one, and there were no issues to puzzle over or to create antagonisms. The Lodge backers engendered no bad feeling, except in the campaign headquarters of Rockefeller, Goldwater, and Nixon.

The genius of this mailing,

as Goldberg saw it, was that it asked so little of the recipient. "We didn't ask them for money," he said, "we didn't ask them to volunteer for anything or to do anything but sign a card and return it. But still we didn't know what to expect by way of returns." Before the end of the campaign nearly ten thousand pledges had been sent back, and they were all forwarded to Saigon. . . .

Members of the Lodge group down to the district leader were given specific instructions to make no statements and engage in no debates on substantive questions. No one was permitted to speak for the Ambassador. Personal attacks were out of the question because their use would be considered villainous, a slur on a patriot who was doing his best for the United States in one of the world's trouble spots. Several times the Rockefeller organization drafted a statement on Lodge, but one was never issued.

The second mailing

included a sample ballot which exactly duplicated the official New Hampshire Republican primary ballot. It showed the recipient how in five steps he could vote for all the delegates favorable to Lodge and write in the name of Henry Cabot Lodge. Also enclosed was a small card— meant to be taken to the polls—with the names of all the Lodge delegates on it. Another card listed the dates and hours at which the Manchester television station would carry a five-minute film spot promoting the Lodge candidacy.

The television film

was clipped from one prepared by the Republican Party for the 1960 presidential election. Four of its five minutes showed President Eisenhower narrating the career of vice-presidential candidate Lodge. However, the film had been edited to fit the new circumstances. To avoid the danger of being charged with deliberate misrepresentation, the film was introduced by a statement describing its origin. Still, the image of Eisenhower with his arm around Lodge's shoulder saying, "I want him . . . ," was not lost on the voters. The final minute of the film demonstrated how the ballot could be filled in with votes for Lodge delegates and the film closed with a hand writing in the name of Henry Cabot Lodge. Using a saturation technique, the Lodge organization spotted the film 39 times in the final twelve days of the campaign. The Manchester station reaches an area inhabited by nearly three-fourths of the people in New Hampshire.

For roughly $3000—five hundred to edit the film and the rest for television time—Goldberg and Grindle got television coverage nearly as good as that for which Rockefeller and Goldwater . . . spent tens of thousands more.

Professor Vasilew sums up: "Primary day . . . 97,000 Republican ballots were cast. Lodge received 35% of them, or 33,000, which was about 13,000 more than Goldwater, his nearest rival. . . . In a six-man field he got more than a third of the vote."

Professor Vasilew cites "a reporter touring New Hampshire to gather material for a post-mortem on the primary and stopping to ask a back country dweller why New Hampshire chose Lodge. 'Dunno,' came the reply, 'maybe, it's because he didn't bother us none.'"

This, however, is not the professor's view, which he expressed in his concluding words: "But the matter which should arouse serious concern, because it could be a portent, is that in a technologically advanced democracy a silent, absent, noncandidate can triumph in so significant an event as a presidential primary in the face of the dedicated campaigning of two other serious contenders who at least most of the time dealt with the issues. In that context the public relations campaign poses a real threat to democratic representative government."

Professor Vasilew misses one central point: that, as regards the presidency, there may be occasions when the office should seek the man. There is surely no "threat to democratic representative government" in that. The professor's logic would make a draft impossible.

For me campaigning used to be a great occupation. I loved the excitement, the competition, the action, and the debating.

194

Later, the dollar cost of campaigning took much of the joy out of it. But there was always one thing which made campaigning fun for me over the years and that was the candor of the voters toward politicians. I think of a visit during one campaign to a small town where I wanted to see a man who was supposed to be the key man there. If he was for you, so I was told, you could not fail to carry the town; if he was against you, you were sure to lose it. This protean individual, let us call him Joshua Robinson, kept the general store. As I entered his store the doorbell jingled; I went up to the counter, extended my hand, and said, "My name is Henry Cabot Lodge; I am running for United States senator and I'd like to have your support." Just then a man came in to buy some plug tobacco, so Mr. Robinson, bald, long-nosed, and equipped with steel-rimmed spectacles, turned away from me to attend to his customer. Thinking that he might not have heard me, I again told him my name and my errand. Once again I was headed off by a lady eager to purchase some shampoo. For the third time I told Mr. Robinson my name and my errand. This time a boy came in to buy some licorice. Again Mr. Robinson ignored me. Finally, I said, "Mr. Robinson, you don't seem to like me very much." And Mr. Robinson replied, "I don't like ya; I don't dislike ya; I just don't give a damn about ya."

This attitude is characteristic of American politics. According to the story, in 1852 the secretary to Franklin Pierce (the only president of the United States to come from New Hampshire and perhaps one of the least distinguished men ever to hold that office) demonstrated it. On the day the convention was meeting in Baltimore, Pierce asked his secretary, a tall, cadaverous Yankee named Hiram, to go down to the telegraph office to see if they had nominated anyone at Baltimore. Hiram went down to the telegraph office, came back a few minutes

195

later and stood in the door with a sour grin on his face and said, "Strange as it may seem and incredible as it may appear, they've nominated you."

The voter has a right to be brutally candid with the politician—and he exercises that right. And the politician has the right to defend himself. Sam Goldwyn is quoted as saying about a critic, "Don't pay any attention to him—don't even ignore him." A heckler once yelled at Al Smith, "Tell them all you know, Al. It won't take long." Al, without hesitation, answered, "I'll tell them all we both know; it won't take any longer."

Gibes at politicians are healthy. They keep a politician sharp. Doctor Johnson said of a man about to be hanged— "Depend on it, when a man knows he is going to be hanged in a fortnight, it concentrates his mind wonderfully."

An example of quick repartee was, according to local folklore, uttered during the Civil War by a Massachusetts politician named Ben Butler. A rare bird (a pro-Union, antislavery, Northern Democrat), President Lincoln had, in accordance with the custom of the times, commissioned him as a general, believing that this would solidify support for the prosecution of the war.

"General" Butler commanded at Norfolk, Virginia, a vital place where ships carrying Confederate cotton destined for England and which had been caught by the Union Navy, were held. One day Butler was seated behind his desk, dressed in his dark blue uniform with two rows of brass buttons. A yellow sash was around his middle, over which was strapped a belt on which hung a large sword. Two lawyers came to visit him representing clients in England who were desperately eager to receive their shipments of cotton then being detained in Norfolk. After the lawyers explained the urgency of the case, according to this unsubstantiated story, they offered Butler

196

$250,000 for himself personally if he would let the shipments go. This was a lot of money.

Butler, sword clanking and brass buttons flashing, rose immediately from his desk, stood erect to his full height of five foot three, and said, "For that insult I am tempted to kick you out of my office, down the stairs to the next street corner and up one flight to the office of my brother who handles just such matters."

Butler also commanded in New Orleans where his troops looted so many knives, forks, and spoons that he became known as "Spoon" Butler. After the war, running for governor of Massachusetts, he was making a speech to a large crowd. His opponent had stationed a boy at the back of the stage with a long fishing pole. To the end of the line which hung from the end of the fishing pole was tied a spoon.

Butler had short legs, a large bald head, a big nose, and a little moustache. While he was standing there speaking, the spoon dangled high up and behind him. He could not see it, but the audience started to giggle. Slowly the spoon descended. Butler continued speaking. In the middle of an eloquent passage, the spoon came into his line of vision. Quickly he grabbed it, put it into his inside coat pocket, and said, "Oh, something I forgot in New Orleans!"

CHAPTER SEVEN

☆　☆　☆　☆　☆　☆　☆　☆　☆　☆

In the Sixties

A few weeks after election day in 1960 I received an invitation to visit the United Arab Republic as the guest of the UAR government. Such an invitation to someone who was completely out of office was extremely generous—and I accepted. This kindness had been instigated by my old friend, former Foreign Minister, now Prime Minister Mahmoud Fawzi, whom I had known at the UN.

Isak Dinesen's *Out of Africa* had long been a favorite book of my wife's and mine and had whetted our imaginations. So we decided to start our African trip in Kenya, going then to Ethiopia and Egypt, and ending in Tunisia. I was then honorary chairman of the Institute of International Education (the private organization which administers the Fulbright Act and sets up local committees to choose students to go to the United States) and I had helped raise the money to build its new headquarters in New York, opposite the UN. The trip would give me a chance to see how the IIE was functioning in these African countries.

We left Europe at Athens in the middle of a May night and at dawn could see Mount Kilimanjaro straight ahead and Mount Kenya off a little to the left, both summits covered with snow. Landing in Nairobi, our first sights were the giraffes grazing on the airport grounds. A few days later we saw lions close by. Our excitement was intense. For us such sights were absolutely mesmerizing.

By the most extraordinary coincidence, we stumbled, while in Kenya, onto the "Dominio di Doriano," a magnificent and enormous farm owned by M. M. Rocco on the shores of Lake Naivasha, north of Nairobi. The Roccos were typical of the group of adventurous Europeans who had settled in Kenya when they were very young, drawn irresistibly by the great spacious life there. Most of these attractive pioneers were British, but there were also Italians and Germans. Mr. Rocco had married Giselle, the daughter of Philippe Bunau-Varilla, mentioned in Chapter 1. She and I were meeting again for the first time in over forty years. They lived with their children in a rose-colored villa reminiscent of Italy with an avenue of cyprus trees leading from the house to the lake. Mrs. Rocco had a particular flair for sculpting animals; I remember a rhinoceros head set in the wall, sticking out from it in a most strikingly lifelike way. The ranch was incredibly fertile. It produced great crops of strawberries and one harvest a month of alfalfa—for the race horses in Calcutta and Hong Kong! One of their problems was the hippopotamuses who came out of the lake at night to eat the alfalfa. At evening hundreds of pink flamingos would settle on the waters of the lake.

The Mau Mau movement was then very active, and within a few years Kenya was to be independent. Europeans were beginning to leave, but the Roccos stayed on.

200

We went north to Nyeri, an immense reservation in which was Tree Tops, a two-story structure some fifteen feet off the ground with a flat roof, built into a grove of seven or eight enormous trees. We climbed a ladder at 4:00 P.M., pulled the ladder in after us, and spent the night. There were cots for resting, but, if the animals were plentiful, not much resting was done. It was on the edge of a lake and next to a place in the ground known as a salt lick (which, I believe, was replenished from time to time) to attract the animals. Artificial moonlight took the place of the real thing when needed.

When we arrived, Tree Tops was covered with bold and active monkeys. We had supper with twenty other guests and, as the sun went down, waited for the animals to appear. Sometimes there are none and sometimes there are many. On our particular evening, May 8, 1961, I counted eighteen elephants, three rhinoceroses, more than thirty waterbuck, forty-five buffaloes, twenty-five wart hogs, one forest hog, one rabbit, and fifty or sixty monkeys. The elephants walked right underneath the house and their backs could not have been much more than three feet away. One could smell them! Talking and smoking were forbidden.

From the right a female rhinoceros and her baby came along at about 11:00 P.M. and started to eat chunks of dirt at the salt lick. (Both rhinoceroses and elephants, I was told, need to have a certain amount of plain dirt in their digestive tracts as roughage.) The mother rhinoceros was digging up the earth with her big horn. Their little beady eyes glinted in the artificial moonlight.

While this was going on—a mother elephant with her young suddenly appeared from behind a large, thick bush on the left. She stood transfixed by the sight of the rhinoceroses. One could sense her annoyance. She had obviously been looking forward to leading her baby to the salt lick and here was an interloper. Her ears stretched out at right angles to her head on either side—a sure sign, I was told, of vexation in an elephant. She was evidently asking herself whether she should charge and push the rhinoceros out immediately or wait. She decided to temporize—the hunter told me that the elephant is the only animal which will have second thoughts—and began marching round and round the rhinoceroses, sounding notes from time to time that were as pure—and as loud—as the blasts of a brass trumpet. At one point the rhinoceros came up behind the elephant with an upward movement of her head, poked the elephant in the stomach with her horn—affecting the elephant no more than a mosquito bite.

After a while a large male rhinoceros appeared from behind a bush on the right. He was almost twice as big as the mother and had a rectangular silhouette similar to that of a brick or a freight car. With his little eyes he surveyed the scene and watched the two lumbering ladies sparring. After studying the situation, he must have decided—in male fashion—that there was nothing much in it for him and that he had better sit it out, because he turned around and disappeared off to the right whence he had come. Indeed I could not even be sure whose side he was on!

Finally, after about two hours, the elephant had had enough. She put down her tusks and charged the rhinoceros. The rhinoceros lumbered away uttering loud grunts of anger and the mother elephant with her baby were in sole possession of the salt lick. The hunter told me that the elephant always wins these contests but the rhinoceros is "magnificently stubborn and stupid" and always has to be pushed out.

From Kenya we went to Addis Ababa, a fascinating place, but where old, abandoned horses stand around in mournful little groups. Nobody feeds or takes care of them and, little by little, they are pushed out into the countryside to graze—where the predators fall on them.

Flying from Addis Ababa to Cairo we flew over Khartoum. We had been to Sudan in 1956 as guests of the government of Sudan. It had been about 100 degrees on the day we were there, but very dry. A wet bath towel hung over the back of a chair became bone dry in a few minutes. We had been comfortably lodged in a onetime British guesthouse and noted that the Sudanese had kept the delightful British customs which make life so pleasant—particularly fresh fish out of the Nile for breakfast onto which we would squeeze the juice of fresh limes, all served up in covered silver dishes. As it hardly ever rains, the night skies look like deep, black velvet. With some Sudanese officials—all over six foot three in height—we had gone to an outdoor night club where sad and bedraggled European women worked as dancing partners.

We arrived in Cairo at 10:00 P.M. and were most hospitably met by the Fawzis. A most efficient gentleman, Colonel Abdel Rahman el Tohany, was placed in charge of us for the duration of our stay, which included a visit to the pyramids, boat trips on the Nile, a visit to Alexandria, inspection of new rural communities, and a call on Prime Minister Nasser. As far as foreign policy was concerned, Nasser said nothing to me that he had not said a thousand times. But the passionate intensity with which he talked about his plans for improvement of rural conditions was impressive. His plans were based on two essential principles: encouraging small land ownership and promoting the basic public services needed for economic and social progress. A community containing a health center, a social center, a school and agricultural center, and public playgrounds was called a "combined unit." They were enthusiastic about an American animal which never gets on page 1 in the U.S.—the Rhode Island red chicken. About three years later in Vietnam I was to meet the same enthusiasm for the American pig. I observed a program for breeding Frisian bulls to improve local pedigrees and increase the production of milk and meat which was being conducted at a beautiful village called Delta Barrages on the Nile, next to one of the major dams.

My last visit to Cairo had been when I was in the army with the U.S. tank crews in 1942 and Cairo was the site of the British Middle East headquarters. The contrast between those days and the vigorous national consciousness of 1961 was striking.

We visited the Gaza Strip and were shocked by the crowded conditions in the refugee camps, but grateful for the hospitality of the governor—Brigadier Ibrahim M. Gad.

We next flew to Tunisia where its Roman ruins, notably Dougga (like Leptis Magna and Sabratha in Libya), are really finer, larger, and more complete than anything we had seen in Europe. The dryness of the air enables these great old, empty, stone cities to endure. We visited Tunis, Carthage, Kairouan, and Sousse. A call on President Habib Bourguiba was the high point. Besides his patriotism, bravery, and spirit of sacrifice, was added good judgment and a sense of moderation.

While on my African jaunt, I received a message from Secretary of State Rusk:

> When the Atlantic Institute meets at Paris, I hope that you will be agreeable to permitting the American Board of the Institute to nominate you for the position of the Institute's Director. This important international group could not, I feel, have a better qualified or more vigorous leader than you. The President, to whom I have mentioned this, believes it would be a fine thing if you agreed to do it and expressed his confidence that you would do an excellent job.
>
> Dean Rusk
> Secretary of State

So for the last half of 1961, all of 1962, and the first half of 1963, I worked part-time getting the Atlantic Institute established—an interesting occupation, particularly as such able and experienced men as the late Will Clayton, the Houston financier, Dr. James B. Conant, former president of Harvard, Sir Oliver Franks and Lord Gladwyn of the United Kingdom, Raymond Aron and Jacques Rueff of France, Kurt Birrenbach of Germany, Vittorio Valletta of Italy, the Fiat genius, Paul Henri Spaak and Paul van Zeeland of Belgium, and Lester B. Pearson of Canada were all involved. I believe its studies of the implications of an expanding European common market, its proposals for strengthening the international monetary system, and its survey of the need to develop education in the less-developed countries (with help from the developed ones), have been valuable. The Institute is still functioning and doing useful work as an idea factory for the Atlantic community.

In June 1963 President Kennedy asked me to be ambassador to Vietnam and I accepted. I believed that many mistakes had been made since 1945 and that if, in that period, the Indochina question had been wisely handled, the United States need never have gone there. In that sense the American presence there was a mistake. In 1963, however, these were all speculations. The reality was that, regardless of how they got there, Americans were in Vietnam and were in combat. To accept, therefore, was a duty. I was to be involved with Vietnam for some five years thereafter.

I appreciate how deep and sincere—and, in many cases, how bitter—are the disagreements over the Vietnam question. This account of my views at that time is therefore submitted with profound respect for many of those who differ and with profound compassion for all those who have suffered so much—American and Vietnamese, military and civilian.

My view was that the people of South Vietnam had a right to exist independently of North Vietnam and that South

Vietnamese rights were being threatened by aggression from North Vietnam.

I believed that it was important wherever possible to support the United Nations Charter and its mandate for the "suppression" of "aggression." I never believed that the Vietnam war was basically a war against communism. It was not an ideological matter. The North wanted to conquer the South. I recognized the demand and need for revolution in both North and South Vietnam to rid the region of the old structures of colonialism and feudalism and to build new structures. The right of the people in the South, however, to build their own structures deserved respect. I thought from the beginning that an exclusively military solution to the Vietnam problem was impossible. To make a long story short and for reasons which will appear, I eventually reached the conclusion that we should withdraw our troops from Vietnam as fast as this could be done in an orderly way and try to negotiate a settlement.

I arrived in Saigon on a rainy night in August 1963. Driving through the hot tropical blackness from the airport to the embassy, the only human beings we saw were soldiers edging the street, but facing the houses, with guns ready to use. Martial law had been declared.

There were excellent people on the embassy staff, headed by the deputy chief of mission, William C. Trueheart, whose advice I heard on everything—with great respect. I also made some new friends in Saigon who widened my understanding of Vietnam, thereby increasing the value of my advice to the president. One such friend was Archbishop Salvatore Asta, the apostolic delegate. There were over a millon and a half Roman Catholics in Vietnam with a proportional number of priests, virtually all of whom were Vietnamese. These priests were in most instances close to the people. Not only were they officially linked to Archbishop Asta, but by dint of his per-

206

sonal qualities, he had won their confidence and their liking. Another friend was Professor Patrick J. Honey of the University of London who had been introduced to me by an energetic and brilliant colonel then on duty in the embassy, John M. Dunn. Professor Honey was that rare man—a highly intelligent Westerner who had thoroughly mastered the Vietnamese language and could discuss abstruse subjects in Vietnamese. He had been coming to Vietnam for two or three months every year for a long time and had the contacts that only years of residence could bring.

Conversations with these men confirmed my impression that, although President Diem had been an effective leader in the past, his rule was clearly entering its terminal phase—regardless of what the United States did. A highly intelligent and well-informed Vietnamese, referring to the reign of terror then under way in Vietnam, had told me in Washington just before my departure that "unless they leave the country there is no power on earth that can prevent the assassination of President Diem, of his brother Ngo Dinh Nhu, and of his sister-in-law Madam Nhu." This prediction turned out to be tragically accurate.

I called on President Diem soon after my arrival. President Kennedy had instructed me to raise a number of matters with him, notably the practices being used by his brother Nhu which, it was constantly and generally said, involved arbitrary imprisonment, torture, persecution of Buddhists, and other cruel and oppressive measures. I also was instructed to bring up especially the idea of having Nhu leave the country. However, no discussion of these matters took place, as President Diem would answer entirely irrelevantly and continue talking at great length on unrelated subjects, refusing all reference to the issues which Washington had asked me to raise.

But he had a most attractive side as well. He was a very

gracious host, as my wife and I found when he took us—a week before his death—on an airplane-helicopter-automobile trip to the high plateau, ending the day at the charming hill town of Dalat. He was courageous and loved his country. Although I had only known him for a few weeks, I was deeply grieved by his death and horrified at the form it took.

On August 25 I received the oft-published cable from Washington saying that the United States must "face the possibility that Diem himself cannot be preserved." The cable said that "the United States cannot tolerate a situation in which the power lies in Nhu's hands"—referring to Diem's brother—and instructed me to "make detailed plans as to how we might bring about Diem's replacement."

My plans initially involved getting in touch, in person or through others, with the generals believed to be interested in overthrowing President Diem so as to learn of their intentions, to get details on the specific troop movements which are often so crucial, and then to see what, if anything, we should do. I was further "authorized to tell the appropriate commanders that we would give direct support in any interim period of breakdown."

I did my best to carry out my instructions, not realizing at the time that they had not been cleared at the highest levels.

On August 25 I suggested that we tell the generals believed to be hostile to Diem that the United States supported Diem, but had grave reservations about Diem's brother and sister-in-law.

On August 28 the State Department told me that it approved of this but it continued to believe that Nhu must go and that a "coup will be needed."

Presumably, these are the words on which was based the accusation, subsequently made so often, that the coup against

Diem was, to quote the *Pentagon Papers*,* "variously authorized, sanctioned and encouraged" by the United States. On August 30 the telegrams of August 25 and August 28 were canceled. This cancellation in effect removed the basis for the charge that the United States government, under the administration of President Kennedy, had "variously authorized, sanctioned and encouraged a coup."

The coup of November 1 was essentially a Vietnamese affair. Because of our lack of involvement in the intricacies of Vietnamese political life, we could not have started the coup if we had wanted to. Nor could we have stopped one once it had started. Our policy, under instructions from President Kennedy, was "not to thwart" a coup. We adhered scrupulously to that policy. I have often wondered why those who leaked the *Pentagon Papers* did not leak the whole story, notably the fact that the August 25 cable was canceled by a message dated August 30. I assume that they did not know about it.

My efforts before the cancellation telegram had shown me that there was little enthusiasm in Saigon, in August 1963, for organizing a coup to depose President Diem. One reason for the apparent reluctance may have been the belief that we Americans knew too much about what was being planned. I sensed a lack of trust in our ability to keep our collective American mouths shut; the anti-Diem generals believed that surprise and secrecy were essential to the success of a coup. The common assumption that the American position was so strong in Saigon that all we had to do was to push the button to set a coup in motion was baseless. Actually, there was no button to push.

* *Pentagon Papers* (Toronto, New York, and London: Bantam Books, 1971), p. 162.

There is no doubt that when a certain point was reached in late October, the embassy, in its efforts to be well informed, was in close touch with the coup plotters. We thought that unexpected events might occur which would require a basic new decision by President Kennedy, in which case it would be vital for him to know as much as possible about the circumstances immediately preceding any such developments. Of course, we were not privy to the conspiracy to murder Diem. (To this day we do not know whether the murder was an act of private revenge or arranged by the coup plotters.) And we did not know until the day of the coup just what the precise moment would be. Being tolerably well informed is not the same as "authorizing, sanctioning, and encouraging" the coup.

The *Pentagon Papers* say that I "authorized CIA participation in tactical planning of the coup." I well remember that I was specifically ordered by the president not to help in the planning, and that I scrupulously obeyed orders. It is hard to believe that this instruction is not in the files.

I did offer President Diem safety under the aegis of the United States and was prepared to give him asylum in my house, to help him enter a new government as a ceremonial figure, or to leave the country.*

* Being worried about the safety of President Diem's two nieces and one nephew (the children of his brother Ngo Dinh Nhu), I assigned a senior foreign service officer, Frederick W. Flott, who could, I believed, be counted on to carry out his mission, to care for them. Mr. Flott fetched the children from Dalat and accompanied them in a special United States government plane from Saigon to Bangkok where they took a commercial flight to Rome. Because they had no passports, I took it upon myself to issue them an impressive looking "travel document" in which I said they were indeed the children of Ngo Dinh Nhu and to which the clear-headed Italian ambassador, Giovanni d'Orlandi, affixed an Italian visa. This document was on thick, expensive-looking paper on which scrolls, eagles, and stars had been engraved and was resourcefully prepared for me by my aide, Kenneth Rogers.

210

The allegation in the *Pentagon Papers* * that "in October we cut off aid to Diem" in order to give a "green light to the generals" is wrong. It was done in order to get Diem to strengthen his political position at home by sending brother Nhu out of the country. Far from trying to overthrow President Diem, President Kennedy was—I thought very properly —engaged in trying to help him get stronger and the government get better.

In fact, in commenting on a suggestion of mine to use our economic aid to bargain for such a better government, the president wired on September 12, "Your #478 is a major paper and has stirred a corresponding effort to concert a proper response here. I want you to know that your courageous and searching analysis has already been of great help and that the strength and dignity of your position on the scene are clear."

We do ourselves a disservice by judging events in East Asia by the same standards which we apply to events in the United States—for example, thinking in terms of a largely nonexistent national "public opinion," talking about a government being "broadly based" and representing all the various "schools of thought," or discussing what policy the Vietnamese would "choose." When I was there, such terms were largely inapplicable in South Vietnam on a nationwide basis.

It is important never to forget that South Vietnam is a land without a Western democratic tradition—indeed, that by our usual way of thinking, it was not a modern nation-state at all. A man in Vietnam would be more likely to say, "I am a Cao Dai or a Hoa Hao" (the names of two Vietnamese sects) than to say, "I am a Vietnamese." It did not occur to most Vietnamese that an election was a good way to decide an important problem. The Confucianist tradition, founded on

* *Pentagon Papers*, pp. 159 ff., 176.

211

the idea of respect for the ruler, holds that a ruler stays in office and gets respect as long as he deserves it. But when, after eight or nine years, he becomes untrustworthy or lazy or cruel —inefficiently authoritarian—someone gets rid of him and the process starts over again. In their tradition, a coup was for them an acceptable way to get a change.

North Vietnam, on the other hand, under Chinese and Russian influence, had become an efficiently authoritarian police state in modern dress, governed with iron control by a small group of determined men. It had created a most effective army. Although North and South Vietnamese are ethnically very similar, it is hard to think of two countries which are more differently organized. About the only thing in common, governmentally speaking, is that neither is a Western democracy.

To conclude this account of my work in Vietnam in 1963 and 1964, I believe the time has come, now that almost ten years have elapsed, to disclose that during the weeks preceding the coup against President Diem, President Kennedy had instructed me not to tell anyone about the cables I was sending to him and the cables he was sending to me, or to reveal any part of their contents. I, of course, fully respected these instructions, which a president has an unquestioned right to give. Clearly senior officials would resent not being in the know and their resentment would be aimed at me. Naturally, I would have liked to have given them these messages, notably to General Paul Harkins, a longtime friend for whose record of distinguished service in war and peace and for whose able career I have the highest admiration. But of course it was my job to carry out President Kennedy's eminently proper orders.

President Kennedy referred to this state of affairs in the following message (not mentioned in the *Pentagon Papers*) to me, dated November 7, ending my secret reports to him:

212

Your message makes a fitting ending to the weekly reports which you have sent in response to our #576 and from now on I think we should be in touch as either of us feels the need. . . . Your own leadership in pulling together and directing the whole American operation in South Viet Nam in recent months has been of the greatest importance and you should know that this achievement is recognized here throughout the government. . . . I look forward to your own visit to Washington so that you and I can review the whole situation together face to face.

With renewed appreciation for a fine job,

John F. Kennedy

The president's instructions not to disclose the exchange of cables between him and me also explained the statement by Secretary of Defense McNamara in his report to President Johnson of December 31, 1963 (*Pentagon Papers*, p. 272) that "Lodge simply does not know how to conduct a coordinated administration . . . he has just operated as a loner all his life and cannot readily change now." A day or two after this was published I received the following letter from former Secretary McNamara:

June 23, 1971

Dear Cabot:

I am told that the New York Times printed a copy of a memo, attributed to me, which, in part, was critical of you. I have not seen that edition of the Times. However, I want you to know that I believed then and I believe now that every American is indebted to you for your service to our nation, both the service before your assignment to South Vietnam and your service during that assignment. I hope that under similar circumstances I too will have the courage, vitality, and sense of duty to accept such an assignment and the wisdom to carry it out as well.

You may use this note in whatever way you wish.
With best wishes,
Bob

I resigned in June 1964 for a number of reasons, foremost of which was that my wife had not been well. My successor was General Maxwell D. Taylor.

I joined forces on my return to the United States with the unsuccessful attempt to bring about the nomination of Governor William W. Scranton of Pennsylvania as Republican candidate for president. I also had many talks with officials in Washington about Vietnam.

In 1965 President Johnson asked me to return as ambassador to Vietnam and I accepted. In 1964, while I was still on duty in Saigon, the team of General Don and General Minh which had overthrown Diem had themselves been overthrown by General Khanh in a coup which seemed to take everyone by surprise—including the Americans. Khanh in turn had been overthrown during Ambassador Taylor's tour. Thus, when I returned for a second tour in the summer of 1965, I found the Saigon government in a state of grave instability and turmoil. The changes of prime minister could only be described as kaleidoscopic. Every time there was such a change, the enemy would infiltrate the govenment. Without stability, the government would soon be subverted from within. Until there was stability, no effort to ward off the Northern aggression could even get started—let alone succeed. Without stability no social progress would be possible. No wonder that, in the United States, both press and politicians clamored for stability in Vietnam. My experience with coups in my first term—and Ambassador Taylor's experiences—led to the inevitable conclusion that the South Vietnamese should give a high priority to establishing a stable and orderly government. South Vietnam seemed to face three choices: to continue the then existing madhouse with results which would in the not-so-long run turn the government of South Vietnam over to Hanoi; to turn the government over to Hanoi immediately; or to try to establish government under a constitution.

In letters, telegrams, and conversations we in the U.S. government who were concerned with Vietnam, were, under the leadership of Secretary Rusk, discussing how the chaos could be ended. Although we were all well aware that Vietnam had no Western democratic tradition, we reached the conclusion that an effort to bring about government under a constitution would have a salutary effect. The job of electing delegates to a constitutional convention, drafting a constitution, and then bringing about its adoption might be catalytic. It might lead to a state of sufficient stability as to make both social progress and police-type security operations possible. The subject also had long interested General Thieu and Prime Minister Ky; they would often bring it up at our frequent meetings on other subjects, and we would exchange views on such matters, for example, as the powers of the Senate or a Bill of Rights. I thus never needed, in the language of diplomacy, to "make a démarche" or to "raise" the question formally. The desire of the Vietnamese officials to bring about government under a constitution was plain.

The aim was not to create a constitution which would bring democracy—clearly an impossible task—but to create something which would start the few politically active people thinking in terms of settling their differences by voting rather than by coups. The mere decision in the summer of 1965 to make a constitution brought with it more orderly processes of government and began to substitute a certain legitimacy for the hurly-burly of unending coups. Of course

215

the constitution did not change the basic nature of Vietnamese society; South Vietnam still retained feudal and Confucianist traits.

The most dangerous situation during my second tour was the so-called Struggle Movement which, at its zenith in the late spring of 1966, had taken over control of Hue and Danang and was a threat in other cities of South Vietnam. The writ of the government of South Vietnam in Hue and Danang simply did not run. This was comparable in gravity to a situation in which the writ of the U.S. government did not run in Detroit and Chicago.

If such Struggler control was allowed to stand, what would prevent them from taking over Qui Nhon, Dalat, and Nhatrang, and going from there to Saigon? The stark truth was that, if the government were driven out of the cities, little would have been left, in view of Viet Cong strength in the rural areas. In such an event it appeared that the northern part of South Vietnam, traditionally known as Central Vietnam, would secede.

The Struggle Movement manifestly helped the Viet Cong, but we believed that the Viet Cong neither started nor ran it. It was operated by certain Buddhist sects and the political machine of an angry political general, General Thi. It was a hard-hitting grab for power and secession based on the ever-present spirit of Central Vietnamese localism.

The irrelevance of modern Western military force to the Struggle Movement in Danang and Hue was illustrated by the way in which the Strugglers took over the city of Danang: A small group of Strugglers came from Hue, called on the chief of police, told him that they intended to take over Danang and that the first step was to take over the police force. They therefore instructed the chief to turn the police over to them by 6:00 P.M. that evening or his wife and children would be kidnapped, his house would be burned down, and he himself would be assassinated. The result of these terrorist measures was that the Struggle committee took over the city.

The III Marine Amphibious Force was a large and magnificent American military force, based a few miles outside of Danang and able to take on any unit of equivalent size. But it was completely out of the game as far as the Struggle Movement was concerned, and had been instructed not to get involved. The defeat of the Struggle Movement, because of its covert character, was an operation in which only Vietnamese could take part. Thus the III Marines could be compared to a net with a large mesh with which to catch whales—which were not the problem. Until Prime Minister Ky moved in with the Vietnamese police and special troops in June, our side did not have the fine-mesh net with which to catch the small but deadly fish of terrorism.

By police methods, by waiting for the right time, by moving by stealth at night and thus achieving surprise, Prime Minister Ky skillfully re-established the authority of the government and with few casualties.

Surely, there was a lesson to be learned from this: that if major stress were placed in a timely way on police and territorial force techniques, the aggression might, eventually, be liquidated without growing into a conventional war and with virtually no loss of American life, no disruption of Vietnamese civilian life, and much smaller Vietnamese uniformed casualties. Instead of looking for massive body counts of rank and file soldiers we would aim at rooting out the highly expert individual terrorist leaders. Also, desertions from territorial forces in Vietnam were much less than from the army. To serve and to fight locally was more in harmony with the rhythm of the rice crop, the teachings of the Buddhist religion, and the Confucianist way of life. I believe that eventually we did move in that direction.

On another level of importance, and a prime responsibility of mine, was the construction of a proper building to house the offices of the American Embassy. These offices were in a most unsuitable and inadequate building situated in a highly vulnerable but attractive and crowded area in downtown Saigon, redolent with the rich smells and noises of the Orient. The building ran right to the edge of the sidewalk so that there was no possibility of building a wall around it. One result of this vulnerability was that in the spring of 1965 an old automobile filled with explosives had been left at the curb which, when it exploded, killed several members of the American Embassy staff, American and Vietnamese, wounded a great many more, and blinded several Americans for life.

The State Department finally found the funds to erect a new building. The plans called for a structure situated well back from the street, with a lawn running from the building to the sidewalk. Study of the security problem convinced me that it was imperative to build a wall along the outside edge of the lawn so that people passing by on the sidewalk would not be able to walk across the lawn. I was so firmly convinced of this that I had decided not to move into the building unless this wall was built. I also stipulated the building of a helicopter landing platform on the roof. Finally, the Department found $25,000 and built the wall (of reinforced concrete) and the helicopter platform.

When the famous attack came at Tet in January 1968 (I was no longer ambassador and was in the United States), the Viet Cong were forced to blow a hole through the wall in order to get into the embassy grounds. This alerted everybody. U.S. troops were brought in by helicopters which landed on the roof. They came down in the elevator and out

218

from the inside of the building onto the lawn—where they found the nineteen Viet Cong commandos caught on the lawn between the building and the $25,000 wall. All of the Viet Cong were killed—but not before they had killed a number of Americans.

Once again my wife's health began to cause me concern and so, after a total of three years, we went to Washington where I served as ambassador-at-large.

During my years in Saigon the daily alerts of Vietnam fully occupied me and, until my return, I knew little at firsthand about American public opinion. As the years went by, I came to believe that although it was still desirable to protect South Vietnam against aggression, the cost in many ways had become so excessive as to make it imperative to negotiate a settlement.

In November 1967, President Johnson called a meeting of former and present officials, named by some junior officers in the State Department the "Wise Old Men," or "WOMs." I was included as a former ambassador to Vietnam. The president called another "WOM" meeting on March 25, 1968, the highlights of which have been published. At this meeting former Secretary of State Dean Acheson said we should not send more troops. I said that the basic thrust of our side's effort, in the future should not be conventional military. It should instead be territorial, constabulary, and counterterroristic— which would make possible a drastic reduction in the number of U.S. troops already there.

Early in 1968 President Johnson asked me to go to Germany as ambassador, where I served almost a year. Germany is a fascinating and potent country and the so-called German question is especially interesting to anyone concerned with international relations. The amenities of life are plentiful. The baroque churches and palaces in Württemberg and Bavaria are unique, as are so many other treats for the eyes and for the ears. One does not live in Germany very long before becoming aware of two sets of feeling, one of which is a pervading sense of sadness about their past under Hitler: *unsere entsetzliche Geschichte*—"our frightful history." The other feeling is of friendship for America.

Leonard Bernstein and the New York Philharmonic Orchestra came to Bonn while we were there. They set the place on fire. Greater enthusiasm there simply could not be. Mr. Bernstein, in addition to his superlative musical performance, said all the right things, complimented his hosts on the acoustics of the concert hall, and came to a reception which we gave in his honor where he was the life of the party. One cannot stress too much the contribution which great artists and music can make to international good will. The more such things happen, the better for all.

A weekend at Johannisberg, the *Schloss* ("castle") belonging to Prince and Princess Metternich, was delightful and unique. The great rangy eighteenth-century mansion of a warm, tan color, with its baroque roof, stands on the peak of a high and steep hill rising out of the north bank of the Rhine. The Rhine generally flows northwest—from Switzerland to Holland. But here it flows due west for some fifty miles. This part is called the Rheingau and the grapes growing here on the north bank of the Rhine benefit from a direct southern exposure which, I was confidently told, makes them more succulent than grapes grown anywhere else. The Metternich's Schloss is squarely in the middle of the finest wine country and its enormous dark cellars contain huge hogsheads full of the delicious Johannisberger Rhine wine.

The house contains artifacts from the days of the original Prince Metternich, the presiding genius of the Council of

Vienna of 1814 and 1815, including a portrait of the Duke of Wellington in the white uniform of a colonel in the Austrian Army. On Saturday night, a full house of guests and neighbors would sit down to dinner in an atmosphere of great gaiety. Presiding over it all was the handsome prince and the beautiful princess.

Looking back over the years since our victory in World War II, one sees that serious mistakes were made with regard to Germany. I remember a visit after the war to that brilliant and magnetic soldier, the commander of the First French Army in World War II, Marshal de Lattre, who was at the time commanding the European armies—the so-called Western Union—with headquarters outside of Paris at Fontainebleau. In his office was a huge map of Western Europe running from the ceiling to the floor. There was a ladder on rollers so that any point of the map could be easily reached. Marshal de Lattre gave me an unforgettable lesson in European geography. Beginning on the shores of the Baltic he ran the length of the present frontier between East and West Germany, pointing out highly strategic terrain features— mountains, swamps, rivers, towns, and crossroads. In every case these strategic features were on the East German side. Evidently, we had not been as well prepared for the end of the war as the Russians had been. It is a happy thing indeed that a Berlin agreement has recently been reached which, by ending harassment, should make the German question more peaceful than it has been at any time since the end of World War II.

My last association with Vietnam came in January 1969 when President Nixon appointed me his representative at the Paris meetings on Vietnam. The essence of the North Vietnamese position at that time was that the Americans must immediately and totally withdraw and, as they closed the door

221

after them, overthrow the government of South Vietnam. That is still the position as this is written—three and a half years later.

As the president's representative, and with the help of two brilliant foreign service officers, Philip C. Habib, now U.S. ambassador to Korea and onetime political counselor with me in Saigon, and Peter Tarnoff, who had also been my aide in Saigon and Bonn, I presented our proposals for peace. They provided for the complete withdrawal of all outside forces from Vietnam within one year, a cease-fire under international supervision, and free elections under international supervision. The communists could, the United States explained, participate in the organization and conduct of these elections and do so as an organized political force. We would accept the results of such free elections, whatever they might be. It was all to no avail.

After a year at the Paris meetings on Vietnam I resigned and returned to Beverly, Massachusetts, because personal matters required that I be based at home. Later, President Nixon asked me to visit the Vatican from time to time as his special envoy. Since June 1970 I have made eight visits. The Vatican contains men of great capacity and dedication, one of whom is our American cardinal, John Wright. Its professional diplomatic corps make it one of the greatest centers of information. Substantial benefits have already come from our relationship: Due in important part to the Vatican, the amount of mail exchanged between American prisoners of war in Vietnam and their families has markedly increased; and the Vatican has also helped world-wide attempts to curb the drug traffic. I am authorized to discuss with the Vatican all matters pertaining to world peace and to the alleviation of human suffering, a formidably wide range. Great benefit can come from such a relationship with the Vatican in the future.

CHAPTER EIGHT

☆ ☆ ☆ ☆ ☆ ☆ ☆ ☆ ☆ ☆

For the Future

Looking back over all I have written here, the words of Ulysses come to mind:

> Much have I seen and known, cities of men
> And manners, climates, councils, governments.

What I have "seen and known" has taught me "much":

In foreign policy we seem to swing to and fro over the years. In my youth Americans did not want to be involved in foreign affairs—or to appropriate money for the military. A reservist going on active duty often went at his own expense. Regular officers on duty in Washington did not wear uniforms.

World War II first taught us the value of collective security. The lesson was repeated after the war when most of us reluctantly concluded that the Soviet Union, under Stalin, sharing neither the basic tenets of the Atlantic community nor our

223

vision of the UN, was expansionist. Many Americans, not thinking very precisely, thought that our effort to keep peace should be directed against monolithic communism—which was really not monolithic at all—instead of focusing on particular cases of aggression, which is always bad whether committed by czars, by commisars, or by democratic politicians.

Now some of us are reacting against those who spoke of monolithic communism. This is perhaps natural. But it must not make us forget the reality of the Soviet presence in the world. One of the agreements recently concluded in Moscow begins by recognizing that the two great nuclear nations, each of which has the power to destroy humanity, have no alternative but to coexist peacefully—because in a nuclear war there are only losers. President Nixon * said that these principles were like a road map, which having now been laid out, could be followed by both nations. The president added,

> However, we must remember that Soviet ideology still proclaims hostility to some of America's most basic values. The Soviet leaders remain committed to that ideology. Like the nation they lead, they are and will continue to be totally dedicated competitors of the United States of America.
>
> As we shape our policies for the period ahead, therefore, we must maintain our defense at an adequate level until there is mutual agreement to limit forces. The time-tested policies of vigilance and firmness which have brought us to the summit are the only ones that can safely carry us forward to further progress in reaching agreements to reduce the danger of war.

Churchill's dictum that "we arm to parley" is still wise.

We must also in the future be more mindful of the UN and

* "Basic Principles of Mutual Relations Between the United States and the USSR," State Department press release.

its stated purposes to "(1) maintain international peace and security, and to that end: to take effective collective measures for the preservation and removal of threats to the peace, and for the suppression of acts of aggression."

These words, I repeat, deserve more respect than they have had. The Charter, after all, is unique, as the code of behavior for governments which the largest number of nations in the world has ever signed and ratified. It is a high-water mark of international organization. Progress in the world toward civilized international relationships can be measured by the degree to which we live up to these words in the Charter. Its admonition to suppress aggression is not limited to neatly organized Western states, but applies also to the more diffuse, less nationalistically organized peoples of the East.

And yet, having said all this, I hasten to warn of the dangers of overstatement, oversimplification, and black and white thinking in so complex a field as international relations. While we should indeed respect the Charter, we can only live up to the Charter's provisions at a price which we can afford. A blind determination to stop aggression regardless of the cost is as dangerous as a blind determination never to suppress it at all. We should ask ourselves in each individual case what are the costs, and measure the cost of acting against the cost of not acting. These are subtle matters, hard to express in headlines. Yet they are vital.

The specifics of foreign relations are not only complicated; in many cases they are known—and should only be known—to a few insiders. While there has been overclassification of government papers and too much secrecy in many cases, it is also often in our best interests to keep some matters secret. We are, after all, in a competitive—not to say adversarial—relationship with other powers where free speech is unknown and where speed and secrecy can give them an advantage.

This is a real dilemma, because free speech is at the heart of our system. The problem is not solved simply by saying that the public has a right to know. The public also has a right to be protected against the dangers caused by injudicious revelation of official secrets.

In spite of some errors, the public men of this last generation (post-World War II) have done better than their fathers' generation (post-World War I). Had they not, there might be no life on our planet today. Undoubtedly we must thank the sheer horror of the hydrogen bomb for at least some of their wisdom. The men of the post-World War I period started from a more difficult position: In 1919 one could hardly see the forces which were to plunge the world into war in 1939. But in 1945 Stalin's ambition was easy to see.

We must also thank our own American commitment to collective security. The Marshall Plan, the Truman Doctrine of 1948, and our prompt response to the aggression in Korea in 1950 all made for a more peaceful world. When to General Marshall's purely military achievements as the world strategist, organizer of armies, and namer of generals in World War II, you add his authorship of the Marshall Plan, he stands out as one of the great men of our century. To have worked in support of his leadership when, as army chief of staff, he was readying the nation for war, or to have helped to enact the Marshall Plan which he, as secretary of state, was proposing, were great experiences indeed.

For the future it appears that protection against a nuclear attack is relatively well in hand. This assuredly cannot be said of the state of our protection against wars of covert terorism —called by some criminal wars, by others revolutionary wars, and, in communist terminology, national wars of liberation. Yet this kind of warfare can conquer the world, as surely as nuclear weapons can. There are great stores of knowledge on this subject in the State Department, the Pentagon, and elsewhere, but some have apparently not yet learned that to defeat a covert, terrorist aggression takes patient, police-type fighting, braided together with an effective political, economic, and social program. This takes time—but casualties are low. It also raises the question of how we can resist wars of covert terrorism without ourselves becoming "counterinsurgents" (or standpatters) and thus mere perpetuators of the status quo. This is surely not a fitting title nor an appropriate occupation for Americans whose political ancestors are the insurgents of Concord Bridge. The challenge is to frustrate the terrorists without thwarting the forces of legitimate social revolution.

Another hope for the future is that we will become more skillful in the endless propaganda war in which we are, however unwillingly, engaged—both in seeing through the fabrications of our adversaries and in presenting our own case. By constant repetition of a few simple ideas, Hanoi has over the years actually made much of the world believe that we were in Vietnam to establish a colonial empire for ourselves and that their side was without a blemish. It is easy to see why seasoned observers have described this as the most massive propaganda campaign since the end of World War II. In my travels since World War II friends of the U.S. abroad, well aware that our motives were not imperialistic, often told me of their regret that we did not seem able to get our argument across.

As I end these comments on international relations I salute the progress made under President Nixon's leadership in bringing about new relationships with Peking and Moscow and shrinking the American manpower involvement in Vietnam. He has also helped in achieving improved access to Berlin, the cease-fire in the Middle East, the settlement of the Okinawa problem with Japan, and treaties with the Soviet Union curb-

227

ing the arms race. Taken together, these things constitute a notable turn away from war.

Here at home one thing has not changed over the years: the lack of trust in government and the cynical belief that government is a tool of special interests. This is, of course, no reflection on any of our presidents, all of whom have striven energetically to make our system work better but who, because of bureaucratic tangles, are not as all-powerful as is commonly thought. The cynicism stems from the way the system itself has developed. Measures to restore public confidence in government are urgently needed. Following are some suggestions to this end:

—To begin with (and to repeat), we should reform our system for electing the president and the vice-president so as to eliminate the very real present possibility that the candidate who gets the most popular votes might also lose the election— an event which has occurred in the past and which, were it to happen again, would dangerously shake public confidence. I believe that the best way to do this is to abolish the Electoral College and count the electoral vote in proportion to the popular vote.

—The nomination of the president and vice-president also raises many questions: Should we continue the convention system, but require delegates to be elected in a nationwide primary held on the same day and under federal law (they are currently all chosen under state law)? Or should we abolish the convention entirely and embark on a nationwide direct primary? The irritation caused by occasional crudities at some conventions should not blur the fact that the convention is a device which has served us well. It provides a forum—and a well-understood procedure—for settling the major party nom-

inations in time for the election so that a change in the office
of chief executive (always a tricky business in any country)
can take place in an orderly way. When one man has an over-
whelming lead for the nomination—as Franklin D. Roosevelt
did in 1936—the convention is the place where this fact can
be registered and acted on. When there is a contest—as between Eisenhower and Taft in 1952, for example—the convention provides the place for settling the contest. When there
is a deadlock, the convention becomes a true "college" where
the party's leading men can meet, talk, and evolve a compromise. Examples of this are the Republican convention of 1920
where Senator Warren G. Harding emerged from the deadlock between General Leonard Wood and Governor Frank
Lowden and, the Democratic convention of 1924 where
John W. Davis emerged from a deadlock of more than one
hundred ballots between William G. McAdoo and Governor
Alfred E. Smith. Two more different men than the hapless
Harding and the distinguished Davis never lived, but each
was the choice of their party's senior men in the attempt to
end the deadlock.

—Closely connected with the election of the president is
the election of United States senators and members of the
House of Representatives. Should we, as has been suggested,
increase the term of members of the House from two to four
years—so that it would be coterminous with that of the president? If so, should we limit the number of terms a member
could serve, say, to two terms—that is, to eight years—thus
ending a member's service in the House and, of course, ending his seniority? Would this change not bring government
closer to the people? And should similar changes be considered
for the tenure of senators?

—These questions are all closely interrelated. Each one has
its complications and each one is fundamental. They have

brought me to the conclusion that there is a pressing need for hearings to be held by the appropriate congressional committees soon. The purpose of these hearings should be to inform and alert public opinion to alternate methods of choosing presidents, vice-presidents, senators, and representatives. The hearings should be as public, as dramatic, and as interesting as possible. The list of witnesses should include political scientists, campaign managers, and office holders. Such hearings, if conducted with imagination, would have a stimulating effect on public opinion. Without public support, attempts to solve problems as fundamental as these will surely fail: Most of them require amending the Constitution, which means a two-thirds vote of both houses of Congress and ratification either by three-fourths of the state legislatures or by three-fourths of state conventions called especially for the purpose. Truly enlightening hearings can create a climate which will make action possible. Action on these vital matters underlies progress in other fields.

—There should be periodic surveys of the federal government for the promotion of economy and efficiency—to get the snarls out of the machinery—similar to the work of the two Hoover Commissions.

—An eye should also be kept on the quality of coordination existing between federal agencies: between the White House, the State Department, the Defense Department, the CIA, and the Disarmament Agency so that, for example, while State is on the verge of reaching an international settlement, Defense, without this knowledge, will not undertake some new military operation.

—The president should also be authorized to veto specific items in appropriation bills. This authority exists in virtually every modern government. In the United States, however, the president must either veto the whole appropriation bill if there is only one feature which is clearly objectionable, thus paralyzing the government, or he must let the objectionable portion also become law.

—The Constitution should be amended so that appointments made by the president in the executive branch would stand unless rejected by a two-thirds vote. This would give the president power and responsibility, while still retaining enough congressional check.

—The major costs of campaigning for president should (I repeat) be paid for by the government, so that public officials will not be under obligation to private persons. This, more than anything else, is what gives rise to the suspicion that government is the tool of special interests.

—We must put the nation on the road to abolishing poverty—and not just depend on something trickling down from the economic activity at the top of the heap. Enactment of some form of President Nixon's proposal for a guaranteed income would benefit the whole community because it would make society as a whole more contented and thus more stable. The goal would be for the employables to have work, for the unemployables to be treated decently, and for all to have proper housing and medical care—without bankrupting the rest of us.

What I have "seen and known" has convinced me that the old political formula of left, right, and center, so commonly seen in Latin countries, and growing in visibility here, is largely inapplicable to important issues in this country. The urgent need is for government which is efficient, trustworthy, far-sighted, and free from selfish influences. Without such government no policy—whatever its ideological hue—can succeed.

In 1976 we will celebrate our two hundreth anniversary as a nation. Now is a good time to look back to see how well we

231

have carried out our stated purposes as set forth in the Declaration of Independence and the Preamble to the Constitution. When we look, we plainly see that the "inalienable rights" of "all men" have not been assured and that the constitutional mandate to "establish justice" has not been carried out.

And yet there are pluses as well as minuses:

During the past fifty years, for example, life expectancy has increased about 50 percent, the working day has been cut one-third, and per capita output has more than doubled. The advances in medical science have made ours a healthier world. Higher education has become a possibility for millions of youths, whereas fifty years ago it was largely confined to a wealthy few. Much social legislation has been enacted. Hitler's attempts at conquest to impose a racist police state were defeated in a terrible war of unprecedented scale. After the war was over, billions of dollars were spent to help our former enemies rebuild. There was the wisdom to begin the United Nations, to construct NATO, and to carry out the Marshall Plan which saved Europe from being overwhelmed. Television, radio, and aviation have revolutionized life. Our gross national product astounds us. We have gone to the moon. The list goes on and on.

Our country has thus shown itself to be strong in many ways, able to solve many problems, and tough enough to take much punishment. One thing, however, which could be disastrous would be the condition described with such somber drama by W. B. Yeats in which "the best lack all conviction while the worst are full of passionate intensity."

Why do I even suggest this dismal possibility? Surely not because there is anything wrong—or even inadequate—about our ideals. They are as noble as when first written into the Declaration of Independence: that "all men are created equal" and have a right to "life, liberty and the pursuit of happiness"

232

—or, thirteen years later, into the Preamble to the Constitution, with its mandate to "form a more perfect union, establish justice, insure domestic tranquility, provide for the common defense, promote the general welfare, and secure the blessings of liberty to ourselves and our posterity."

But there must be enthusiasm for these ideals. Otherwise, enthusiasm for what is bad will surely triumph over lack of enthusiasm for what is good. Without enthusiasm—without human sympathy—words are pretty dry. In all candor, have we this enthusiasm today?

If, prizing our ideals, we move with feeling, we will find the strength of mind and will to make the needed governmental changes, to decide what our priorities should be and to unify the country once again. Then we will find that, invigorated, our ideals have an unlimited potential with which we can, God willing, solve our problems, stubborn though these problems are.

This utterly basic enthusiasm must come from the feelings of the people. It cannot be done by leaders. "We the people," to use the phrase in the Preamble to the Constitution, are crucial. In the last analysis it is up to each one of us to make our nation practice what it preaches and live up to its ideals.

☆ ☆ ☆ ☆ ☆ ☆ ☆ ☆ ☆ ☆

Appendix

In the interest of completeness,
the publisher submits this Appendix.

Senator Taft's Analysis

(New York Times, November 25, 1959)

WASHINGTON, Nov. 24—Following is the text of an analysis of the 1952 Republican Presidential contest, prepared in the fall of that year by the late Senator Robert A. Taft, Republican of Ohio, who lost the nomination to Dwight D. Eisenhower:

I am writing this brief analysis of the result of the 1952 Republican Convention and the several reasons for that result. There is a tendency to lay too much stress on particular circumstances at the convention and exaggerate the importance of events which made headlines at the moment. I don't want to have any of my supporters blamed for the result and charged with the mistakes which they did not make or which did not really affect the result. I don't want my supporters to feel that there were any serious mistakes of omission and that some striking move would have solved the whole problem.

The result of the convention came far more from underlying causes which had operated steadily for eight months, and continued to operate at Chicago. First, it was the power of the New York financial interest and a large number of business men subject to New York influence, who had selected General Eisenhower as their candidate at least a year ago. There was a strong and substantial minority of Taft supporters among business leaders, but they were a minority, particularly in the East.

Second, four-fifths of the influential newspapers in the country were opposed to me continuously and vociferously and many turned themselves into propaganda sheets for my opponent. Of course, this was not true of the McCormick papers, The Wall Street Journal, The Omaha World Herald and The Los Angeles Times. The Philadelphia Inquirer, the Hearst papers and the Knight papers remained neutral. But most other Republican papers were almost campaign sheets for Eisenhower and were supplemented by the violent support of every New Deal and so-called independent paper. Like the editors, the majority of Republican Governors were sold on Eisenhower support, although a majority of Senators and Congressmen were in my favor. However, the Governors had far more political influence on delegates.

Two-Man Fight

These underlying causes operated throughout the campaign and at the convention.

The convention result, after all, depended far more on the number of delegates than it did on changes of opinion at the convention, which at so many conventions are likely finally to result in a nomination. A long and intense campaign almost entirely between the supporters of General Eisenhower and myself had lined up nearly all the delegates on one side or the other, except those pledged to Warren, Stassen and McKeldin [Earl Warren, Harold E. Stassen and Theodore R. McKeldin, then Governor of Maryland]. It was a two-man fight.

Going back through the campaign, the primary results were generally favorable to that candidate who had the support of the organization and the newspapers. The primary results were favorable to Eisenhower in the East—in New Hampshire, Massachusetts, Pennsylvania and New Jersey; and this had a substantial effect on all New England, New York and Delaware delegates. The primary results were favorable to Taft West of the Alleghanies in West Virginia, Illinois, Wisconsin and Nebraska. This had a substantial effect, of course, on Indiana, Kentucky and many other Western states. Where there were no primaries, the convention results for Eisenhower in Washington, Colorado and Iowa were more than matched by Taft conventions in many other Western states. The Oregon primary helped Eisenhower on the Pacific Coast.

The influences operating, which I have described above, were such that I had to have a pretty clear majority in order to hold a lot of marginal delegates. We probably would have done better if we had put on a real primary campaign in Pennsylvania, New York, Michigan, Oregon and some other states. The difficulty was the tremendous expense involved in any such program and the lack of time to make an adequate campaign against the newspaper

238

influences. Even in South Dakota we almost lost because the three leading newspapers were for Eisenhower.

Reviews Delegate Strength

The net result, after the primaries were over, provided an estimate of 604 delegates for Taft and about 400 for Eisenhower, with 128 for other candidates and 86 uncommitted, largely in Pennsylvania and New York. But this was never a firm estimate, and we knew that even though this number of delegates had expressed a preference for me they might be persuaded otherwise. In this estimate of 604, we counted on twenty-seven delegates from Michigan who favored me at the time of the Michigan convention and afterwards, seventeen from New York, nine from New Jersey, twenty-eight from Texas, ten from Louisiana. I saw this number of delegates in New York and New Jersey personally and had definite statements that they would vote for me, we did not count on Fine's delegates. [John S. Fine, then Governor of Pennsylvania.] It was always clear, therefore, that while we had a hard core of 500 delegates, there were others who were subject to persuasion and pressure. The Michigan estimate was particularly uncertain as long as [Arthur E.] Summerfield tried to hold Michigan as a unit.

To match up possible losses from these delegates, we worked on Governor Fine, Governor McKeldin and numerous uncommitted delegates in New York, New Jersey and other states. We also had assurances of twenty-five from California if Warren ever released them. In spite of every reasonable effort, we did not persuade McKeldin, Fine or Summerfield. Because of strong pressure by the Governors of New York and New Jersey [Thomas E. Dewey and Alfred E. Driscoll] we lost most of the delegates who had given assurances of support in those states. We did hold nine votes out of fifteen favorable Taft supporters after McKeldin accepted an invitation to nominate Eisenhower. The number of California delegates on the Georgia contest was only eight instead of fifty-five because of pressure from the Governor [Earl Warren] and Senators [then William F. Knowland and Richard M. Nixon] from California.

APPENDIX

Couldn't Hold Votes

By the time the convention opened, we reduced our estimates in Michigan by nine discounting Summerfield's defection, Delaware by three, Oklahoma two, Virginia two and Texas by six by reason of the compromise I proposed. These losses were made up by sixteen additional contest delegates and gains in Rhode Island, Connecticut, Massachusetts and a few other states, but our estimate of 607 was again based on New York, New Jersey and Michigan delegates, as well as including fifty from the contested states of Georgia, Louisiana and Texas. It was clear, therefore, when the convention began that if Warren, Stassen and Eisenhower all ganged up on us on preliminary votes, we might not be able to win unless we held on to every vote, or replaced them with additional votes. Neither of these results were we able to achieve.

The first question arose on the change in the rules contrary to every principle of parliamentary procedure. The whole strategy of the other side was to change the rules and get enough votes to steal all the contested delegates, and it was difficult to see how this could be prevented if the Eisenhower people were supported by the Warren and Stassen forces. They did obtain their support because apparently the Warren and Stassen forces felt that their own success depended on a deadlock, and that this action might bring about a deadlock. It probably would have been better to agree to the rule, but, of course, the loss of votes would make the contest fight more difficult. It was probably a mistake to take a vote because it showed that the combined forces against us controlled the convention, but even a concession on our part would also have been regarded as a sign of weakness. On the rule vote we held practically all the Taft states, but were unable to withstand the Summerfield pressure in Michigan, the Dewey pressure in New York and the Fine pressure in Pennsylvania. Fine forced his own representative on the Credentials Committee to reverse the stand he had taken after hearing the evidence.

The key vote came on the Georgia contest, where we lost the equivalent of seventeen votes because of the new rule, but we picked up nine Taft votes in Maryland and eight in California in spite of strong pressure from McKeldin and the Governor and

240

Senators from California. On the other hand, we fell below our estimates in New York, where all but four delegates finally voted against us, and we lost from our estimates four in Michigan, three in New Jersey, three in Nebraska and single votes in other states. We were thirty-eight votes short of winning the Georgia contest, and apparently the same vote would have prevailed in the contest on Texas. Some of this defection may have resulted from the loss of morale on the rules vote, but it seems unlikely. Some Taft delegates couldn't or wouldn't recognize that the Georgia vote was really the first vote on the nomination. Every Eisenhower delegate knew what his job was, and pressure was strong in the states where we had to gain votes.

After the Eisenhower forces, with the assistance of Warren and Stassen, took thirty-nine votes away from us and gave them to Eisenhower, in addition to eleven Louisiana votes lost in the credentials committee, our prospective strength on the first ballot fell well below his strength, and he had all the bandwagon advantage which we would otherwise have had. It is hard to see how we could have won the Georgia contest unless we converted Fine or Summerfield or McKeldin, or held our full strength in New York and New Jersey.

I have referred to the underlying forces which operated not only during the campaign but at the convention. The truth is that we were up against a tremendous publicity blitz led by four-fifths of the newspapers of the country, and all the magazines. Most of the Governors also lent themselves to this propaganda and in states where we did not have a majority we had difficulty in getting any votes at all because of the pressure of the Governors. It is remarkable that as many as 500 delegates stood firm against this tremendous pressure, even after the bandwagon was rolling.

The control of the press enabled the Eisenhower people to do many things which otherwise could not have been done. The making of a moral issue out of the Texas case was only possible because every internationalist paper sent special writers to blow up a contest which ordinarily would have excited a few days' interest and would have been settled fairly by the National Committee and the Credentials Committee. If there was a moral issue, my suggestion that I be allotted only the district delegates clearly not contested, and that representatives of both sides discuss the whole matter in detail, district by district, certainly should have destroyed that issue. But the press was completely unfair in their treatment of it. Adverse national committeemen frankly admitted that they could not even sit down and talk about the merits of the various Taft contests because it would deprive them of the smear issue. Zweifel people had a sound moral claim that the Democrats had taken over Republican primaries. [Henry Zweifel, then the Republican National Committeeman from Texas, was a Taft supporter.] The only way we could get it before the public at all was by advertisements.

Scores 'Eisenhower Press'

In the same way the Eisenhower press made a moral issue of the change in rules, although it was contrary to all parliamentary procedure, and was admittedly proposed only for this convention because of the danger of making it a permanent rule.

Also the Eisenhower press, although usually adverse to the growth of television, played up the exclusion of television from the National Committee as though it involved an intention to steal delegates in secret although the proceedings were public and all the American press were present to watch what happened.

It is all very well to say that we should not have permitted these issues to be created, but the alternative was surrender on matters in which we were in the right, and if there had not been these issues the publicity firms would have invented others to be shouted by the pro-Eisenhower press.

A study of the primaries will also show that the metropolitan newspapers had a tremendous effect on the results in the primaries and conventions, far more than they do on general elections. Eisenhower victories were always ballyhooed and Taft victories played down.

My conclusion, therefore, is that we had practically to secure a very substantial majority of the total number of delegates to win, and that the net result of the primaries was to give us a very thin majority, if any.

At one point in the convention it was suggested that I retire and turn over my delegates to General MacArthur or some other candidate. Any such move, of course, was impossible before the first ballot. It would have been a surrender of principle and a betrayal of thousands of workers and millions of voters who supported me during the eight-months campaign. Furthermore, these delegates were built up as Taft delegates, and I had no power to transfer many of them to anybody. It would, of course, have been an indication of weakness and probably would have resulted in the nomination of Eisenhower almost by acclamation. There was no evidence that anyone else had any substantial support in addition to that which I had.

Of course, if a deadlock had been created after the first ballot, I would have been glad to reconsider the whole situation and would have been glad to withdraw in favor of some other candidate holding my general views, if it had been clear that I could not be nominated and that he would have been stronger on the second ballot than I. There was a tentative agreement on the part of the Warren and Stassen forces to recess the convention after the first ballot.

Graduation Address, West Point

(June 3, 1959)

For 157 years America has looked to the graduates of West Point to lead her through the valley of danger. Whoever is stirred by the recognition that duty is a summoning word; and whoever is moved by the thought of the millions of officers and men who march through the pages of American history under the leadership of Grant and Sherman; of Pershing; and of Eisenhower and Mac-Arthur, must thrill at being in this place where such leadership was forged.

The French essayist Montaigne four hundred years ago said:

"I would rather know the truth of the talk the general had in his tent on the eve of battle than the speech he made the next day to his army" after the victory.

This statement has vivid meaning for me because I have heard some speeches by generals after the victory and they were good. But I have also been in the general's tent on the eve of battle—which is one place where you appreciate the essence of the West Point tradition.

West Point's motto—"Duty, Honor, Country"—inspires its graduates, to be sure. But it is a noble watchword for all Americans because implicit in it is the idea of selflessness, of striving in behalf of something bigger than yourself.

Justice Holmes points out that "The reward of the general is not a bigger tent, but command." Yet there is a state of mind which is interested in getting the credit for what has been achieved, or in getting the perquisites of rank.

But the finer state of mind is that which wants above all to get the job done; which does not ignore danger but refuses to take counsel of its fears. It is expressed in the words of Tennyson which are inscribed over the Antarctic grave of the British explorer Scott, who died on his way to the South Pole: "To strive, to seek, to find, and not to yield."

244

This spirit of selflessness and striving commands the respect of Americans. Because of it West Pointers can repeatedly make great demands on young Americans thought by too many to be soft and self-indulgent.

This spirit of selflessness and striving is also a vital part of what makes America unique and admired by the nations of the world.

For I ask you to take it from a man who has spent much of his life in foreign relations, that what the world admires about America is not the angle player or the corner cutter or the smart aleck, but the man with a code—generous and high-principled—a code by which he lives. You know that at moments it is as difficult to give an order as to obey one. Yet you are equipped to do both because, as West Pointers, you have such a code.

You are on the threshold of great careers—richer in the true sense of the word than any purely money-making occupation could possibly be. They will be richer in terms of the reward that you get during your life; richer in honor and in satisfaction for responsible work well done; and richer in the meaning which they will give to human life when you measure that life's importance in the scale of eternal values.

The daily grist of talk about missiles, necessary though they are, must never let us forget that missiles can never replace men.

Four hundred years before the birth of Christ, Pericles said this about the soldiers who had died in war:

> They faced the foe as they drew near him in the strength of their own manhood; and when the shock of battle came, they chose rather to suffer the uttermost than to win life by weakness. So their memory has escaped the reproaches of men's lips, but they bore instead on their bodies the marks of men's hands, and in a moment of time, at the climax of their lives, were rapt away from a world filled, for their dying eyes, not with terror but with glory.
>
> Such were the men who lie here and such the city that inspired them. We survivors may pray to be spared their bitter hour, but must disdain to meet the foe with a spirit less triumphant. . . .
>
> They gave their bodies to the commonwealth and re-

245

ceived, each for his own memory, praise that will never die, and with it the grandest of all sepulchres, not that in which their mortal bones are laid, but a home in the minds of men, where their glory remains fresh to stir to speech or action as the occasion comes by. For the whole earth is the sepulchre of famous men.

West Point has long had a "home in the minds of men." Indeed, it still has. For, in spite of all our unremitting efforts, the world is dangerous and catastrophes, large and small, can happen.

We all strive so that no war, large or small, shall occur any-where. Your military readiness—your ability not to shrink from any possibility, however bitter—is vital to that striving and to all our hopes for freedom. If, despite our striving, war starts to smolder, we look to West Pointers for the leadership which will meet and defeat the shock of violence where it occurs.

And if, in spite of all our efforts, the worst violence should happen, we look to West Pointers to stand up amid the wreckage —even before the fumes of war have cleared away or the wounded have been tended or the dead have been buried—to take command and save our nation. We count on you for the hard, steely resolve which will never yield.

Yours, therefore, can be the triumph—and the glory—of which Pericles speaks. And because of that our nation holds you in honor every day of its life.

As you begin your careers of leading America through the valley of danger, I salute you and wish you well.

Dedication Address, Guggenheim Museum

(New York, October 21, 1959)

Sir Winston Churchill tells us of the time in 1820 when the great English statesman, Canning, resigned and a Tory lord declared with relish: "Now we have got rid of those confounded men of genius."

This remark comes to mind because Frank Lloyd Wright, the architect of this building, was unquestionably a man of genius who undoubtedly irritated many men during his life as Canning had irritated the Tory lord. In a very different field Solomon Guggenheim was a genius too.

Today in this place we give thanks that we have *not* got rid of men of genius—on the contrary, by their works, they are very much with us.

Americans know that it is a great source of strength for a country to be a place in which a man can be a genius, in which the kind of controversy which Frank Lloyd Wright provoked can flourish, and in which we are not condemned to a style of art called "socialist realism" which exists because the political bosses like it.

This kind of museum, therefore, is only possible in a free democracy. There are many other great and good things which justify the existence of a free democracy. But freedom for artists to express themselves is certainly one of them.

I do not know whether the writings of e.e. cummings irritate or stimulate you, but he has made one statement about the artist which I think illustrates the point that an artist cannot flourish in a totalitarian autocracy which is run in accordance with a rigid doctrine where everything is explained by an arbitrary theory and where the individual citizen must follow the party line.

cummings said that an artist is "a no mere whenfully accreting

247

APPENDIX

mechanism, but a givingly eternal complexity—neither some
soulless and heartless ultra-predatory infra-animal nor any
understandingly knowing and believing and thinking automaton,
but a naturally and miraculously whole human being—a feelingly
illimitable individual; whose only happiness is to transcend himself, whose every agony is to grow."

We welcome this museum and the works of art in it and we
thank the Solomon R. Guggenheim Foundation for making it all
possible. We salute this museum and its contents as wonderful
things in themselves—and also as symbols of what marvels can be
created in a society in which men are truly free.

Lodge's Stands on Key Issues

(*Congressional Quarterly, August 8, 1960*)

Foreign Policy

Mutual Security—"My years at the UN convince me that many of the peoples on the sidelines—in Asia, Africa and the Middle East—do not by any means take it for granted that the western style of freedom is better than Communism. They don't listen much to what we *say* about Communism, but they care a great deal what we *do* for the national independence and better material life which they desire." Oct. 9, 1959.

Why should we have mutual security programs? "For one thing, there *is* a duty incumbent on the rich to help the poor. Secondly, there *is* a humane obligation on all men to help people who are suffering. Thirdly, . . . there is the certainty . . . that if we are 'good bankers' . . . and help these countries get started, it will be a great asset to us in the long run. . . . Fourthly, if we don't help them and they fall into the hands of the Soviet Union, we have done ourselves a very bad turn indeed. . . . Appropriations for economic programs abroad are as vital to our national existence as the money which we appropriate for the diplomatic service or for our military services. Thus self-preservation is one motive for them. But our principal motive should be love of our fellow man. There is no inconsistency between the two." Feb. 12, 1959.

Multilateral aid given through the UN has "definite advantages over our own bilateral program. . . . We put up no more than 40 percent of the aid money contributed. The rest comes from other UN member states. . . . The UN recruits experts from 65 countries—not just the U.S. . . . These UN programs are proof against the suspicion which our opponents are always trying to arouse—that the U.S. may have hidden motives for helping other countries." Oct. 9, 1959.

Eastern Europe—Lodge expressed his "conviction that the

249

Russian tactics of bullying and intimidation in Berlin demonstrate what a ghastly error and what a tragic miscalculation were made at the end of the war when we withdrew our troops from what is now the Russian zone of Germany. It also shows the pressing need for prompt military preparedness if actual harm to American men, women and children in Berlin is to be prevented." April 2, 1948.

"Poland was sold down the river at Yalta to bring Russia into the war against Japan. Our statesmen had the rare opportunity to rescue Poland from its tragic and historic role as the buffer between Germany and Russia, but they fumbled the ball." Aug. 30, 1952.

Presidential Powers—Concerning the Bricker Amendment (to restrict Presidential treaty-making powers): "Certainly this is not the time of all times in the history of our country to deprive the President of the authority our Constitution intends for him to have as our spokesman on foreign policy." Jan. 30, 1954.

On President Truman's dismissal of Gen. Douglas A. MacArthur as Supreme Commander in the Far East: "General MacArthur is a brilliant soldier with a record of service to his country which is unique. Americans will always be grateful to him. It is a great pity that, due in large part to Administration bungling and lack of foresight, differences arose which made it clearly impossible for him to continue, but the civil power—even though we lack confidence in those who hold it—must, under our system of government, be supreme over the military." April 11, 1951.

Soviet Challenge—The U.S. should accept Khrushchev's challenge of peaceful competition in many fields. If the American people work hard to make their own system succeed, they may reverse Khrushchev's prediction that the grandchildren of present-day Americans will live under Communism. "We need to have a great national purpose. . . . A good idea like freedom sitting passively in a fortress will certainly be defeated by a bad idea which is on the march." While the Communist challenge to the free word is serious, "there is an even bigger challenge and that is the challenge presented by the millions of peoples in underdeveloped lands. . . . We have a great powerhouse of talent in our own country which, if really put to work, could do big things. . . . Every American school child of more than average

ability might learn at least one foreign language thoroughly."
Some college graduates "might learn to speak such languages as
Arabic, Hindi, Urdu or Swahili. . . . Able students preparing for
the professions . . . might organize themselves into a nationwide
foreign-service reserve, preparing to spend perhaps five years of
their careers working in the hospitals, industies and univesities of
foreign countries." Oct. 9, 1959.

United Nations—"There's one great difference" between the
United Nations and the League of Nations. "The Covenant of
the League, under Article X, gave the League the power to put
the troops of a country into combat. This was the rock on
which the League foundered. My grandfather, in the Senate,
insisted that the U.S. reserve this right, with the result that this
country didn't join the League. The founders of the UN
remembered this, and the UN can't put a country's troops into
combat without its consent. . . . The UN, in short, is more
realistically based than the League. . . . I don't believe that you
can go much farther than the UN at this time. . . . But we must
go this far. If we didn't have a United Nations we would all be
trying to invent one." June 1960.

Domestic Problems

Civil Rights—"If we are to win the struggle for the minds of
men—particularly in Africa and Asia—we must show at home
that we practice what we preach about equal rights for all, and
that what we do is animated by spiritual values." Feb. 12, 1959.

"Our greatest single weakness with regard to the outside world
is the violations of civil rights which are still committed against
members of racial minorities in this country. . . . When the
world press carries one newspaper story about one Negro being
brutally treated, we do ourselves more harm than the Soviet
Union does with all the distortions of its propaganda." June 1960.

Loyalty—"It cannot be stressed too often that the sole purpose
of all loyalty investigations must be to ferret out disloyal persons.
It must never allow itself to be used to carry out some hidden
purpose of creating a political result here at home. . . . If such
a purpose exists, it merits unreserved condemnation." April 3,
1950.

APPENDIX

In advocating his proposal of a bipartisan commission to review charges of disloyalty by State Department employees, Lodge said: "In the struggle for existence in which the U.S. is engaged, the State Department is the front line of our defense. It is thus essential that confidence in the State Department be restored for once and for all. Confidence cannot be achieved by investigation of the Executive by the Executive, . . . (or) by Congress undertaking an investigation which it has neither the time nor the training nor the facilities to perform." A bipartisan, independent investigation, responsible to Congress, "will result in cleaning out the unfit and in ending any unjustified suspicion of the many fine men and women who work in the State Department." Jan. 15, 1951.

"Of the 3,000 employees of the United Nations, 1,800 are Americans, and the first thing I did on becoming U.S. representative was to arrange for the fingerprinting of every one of those 1,800, and for having them screened by a special U.S. commission in accordance with Civil Service and FBI procedures. Today, every single one of them has been screened and we have set up a procedure for the future. . . . When there are so many good Americans to choose from there is no excuse whatever for employing one single American Communist." April 29, 1956.

Religion in Politics—At the New York dinner of the Society of Friendly Sons of St. Patrick: "Four statewide campaigns in Massachusetts enable me to speak with some authority about the breadth of view and the refusal of the modern American of Irish descent to allow his participation in civic affairs to be distorted or limited by a narrow group outlook. This breadth of view is in contrast with those who raise questions about the religion of a candidate for office, and thereby not only work against the general national interest, but also do violence to the Constitution of the United States." March 17, 1960.

Social Welfare—"In recent years we have taken important steps toward the establishment of a well-rounded, integrated Social Security program. Workmen's compensation for many years has provided financial aid to those who have suffered from injuries sustained during the course of their unemployment. Unemployment compensation aims to protect the unemployed from loss of wages. Old-age pensions are being developed which will safeguard our people from the hazards of insecurity. A well-conceived

252

health-insurance program should bring measurably nearer the day when the American people will be physically fit." Feb. 24, 1947.

Lodge outlined a program for a modern Republican party in an Atlantic Monthly article: "We Republicans should say to the voter: We offer you a welfare society without a welfare state; we offer you a self-liquidating plan. We think the desire for security is normal and human and good, in war and in peace, and that we can have it without red tape, without bureaucracy . . . without sacrifice of opportunity, and without loss of personal liberty." The Republican party should not return to a position of "unmistakable conservatism, dedicating itself to a determination not to compromise with New Dealism." Such a suggestion "is anchored to a dead past." Lodge proposed tax revision designed to increase venture capital and aid small businessmen, rewarding those businesses which lower prices and increase production and stabilize employment. The Lodge proposals included a wide civil rights program including elimination of segregation in housing and educational projects financed by the Government, federal aid for hospital construction, widened Social Security coverage, amendment of the Taft-Hartley law to eliminate "those clearly proven defects in the law which are causing immediate hardships and inequities," and a balanced budget to insure a stable currency. March 1950.

Explaining his vote against a federal aid to education bill: "For one thing, it made it impossible for children in non-public schools to receive the aids to child health which children in public schools receive. In a state like Massachusetts, where almost half the children go to non-public schools, this is actually a serious discrimination against the whole community. The entire Nation needs healthy children regardless of religious differences." Lodge said he also opposed the measure because the allocation of funds "enormously favored the South" at the expense of states like his own, and because "the bill sanctioned Jim-Crowism in education in the South." Feb. 22, 1949.

Lodge Replies to Soviets

Examples of replies made by Lodge to Soviet charges against the U.S. before the UN:

March 11, 1953—Soviet delegate Andrei Y. Vishinsky charged

253

that "you (the U.S.) are going to lose Asia, anyway." Lodge's reply: The U.S. is not trying to "get" Asia; it does not think of Asia "as populated by slaves to be controlled by outside nations." If Moscow would stop thinking of Asia "as a prize in power politics" and try to help its peoples, "we would be taking a big step toward peace."

Oct. 12, 20, 1959—Soviet delegate Vasily V. Kuznetsov charged the U.S. was violating the "spirit of Camp David" and seeking "to worsen the international atmsophere, poison the situation in the UN and perpetuate the notorious cold war" by bringing up the Tibetan question in the UN. Lodge's reply: "We have been asked to believe that it is all right for Chinese Communists to kill Tibetans but that it is a provocation for us to talk about it." Addressing himself to the situation within Tibet, Lodge said, "We have the spectacle of these deeply religious people, their monastéries laid low and their priests and leaders slaughtered and disgraced, being driven into so-called people's communes. . . . We have an opportunity now to prove . . . that neither thousands of miles of distance nor ingenious arguments nor violent words nor faintness of heart can deter us from our duty to a brave people in their time of agony. If they are not afraid to fight and die, let us at least not be afraid to speak the truth."

May 23, 1960—Answering Soviet charges of U.S. aggression in the U-2 inteligence overflight of the U.S.S.R., Lodge said: "Here is a government, well known for it expansionist proclivities and armed to the teeth, which . . . has repeatedly used force . . . in its relations with other sovereign states. . . . When such a government insists on secrecy it is in effect also insisting on preserving its ability to make a surprise attack on humanity. . . . If it should ever be accepted that the Soviet Union can maintain a double standard whereby they have thousands of spies and subversive agents everywhere while protesting one single harmless observation flight, the free world would surely be in great and peculiar danger."

Lodge's Key Votes as a Member of the Senate, 1937–52

Agriculture

1938—Federal Crop Insurance Act, providing for crop insurance on wheat. Lodge AGAINST. Passed, 59–29 (D 55–14; R 3–13 *), Dec. 17.

1942—A bill to reduce the ceilings on prices of agricultural products, as a wartime anti-inflation measure, from 110 percent of parity to 100 percent of parity. "Farm bloc amendment" to include labor costs in computing parity. The effect of the amendment was to offset, to some extent, the reduction of the ceilings. Vote on amendment. Lodge AGAINST. Agreed to, 48–43 (D 31–30; R 15–13), Sept. 29.

1949—Support farm prices at 90 percent of parity, instead of setting up a flexible support program at 75 percent to 90 percent of parity. Lodge AGAINST. Rejected, 26–45 (D 18–23; R 8–22), Oct. 7.

1952—Cut funds for soil conservation payments to farmers from $250 million to $150 million, and limit payments to individuals to $2,500. Lodge announced FOR. Rejected, 23–35 (D 5–29; R 18–6), June 6.

Civil Rights, Immigration

1949—Sustain Vice Presidential ruling that the procedure for cutting off debate and bringing an issue to a vote ("cloture") could be used on a motion to consider amending the cloture rule itself. Lodge FOR. Senate failed to sustain Vice President, 41–46 (D 25–23; R 16–23), March 11.

1950—Force a Federal Fair Employment Practices Commission measure to the floor for a vote by invoking cloture on debate. Lodge FOR. Two-thirds vote required. Rejected, 52–32 (D 19–26; R 33–6), May 19.

1952—McCarran-Walter Immigration and Nationality Act.

* Party breakdowns here and in other votes do not include independents or minor party members.

APPENDIX

Passage over President Truman's veto. Lodge announced AGAINST. Veto overridden, 57–26 (D 25–18; R 32–8), June 27.

Defense

1938—Increase the size of the U.S. Navy. Lodge FOR. Passed, 56–28 (D 49–17; R 7–7), May 3.

1948—Establish a peacetime military draft for men of 19–25. Lodge FOR. Passed, 78–10 (D 41–2; R 37–8), June 10.

1951—Kill universal military training provision of draft-extension bill. Lodge AGAINST. Rejected, 20–68 (D 2–44; R 18–24), March 9.

1951—Troops-to-Europe bill. Amendment stating the sense of the Senate that no ground troops beyond the four divisions planned should be sent to Europe without Congressional approval. Lodge AGAINST. Agreed to on reconsideration, 49–43 (D 11–35; R 38–8), April 2.

Education

1947—Amend National Science Foundation bill to make patents on federally financed inventions available to all free. Lodge AGAINST. Rejected, 28–50 (D 26–7; R 2–43), May 19.

1947—Create a National Science Foundation. Lodge FOR. Passed, 79–8 (D 37–2; R 42–6), May 20.

1948—Amendment to prohibit religious or private schools from receiving federal education-aid funds. Vote on amendment. Lodge AGAINST. Rejected, 5–80 (D 4–35; R 1–45), March 31.

1948—Grant $300 million a year to states to help finance schools. Lodge AGAINST. Passed, 58–22 (D 31–5; R 27–17), April 1.

1949—Grant $300 million a year to states to help finance public schools and to help pay for textbooks and bus service for religious and private schools. Lodge FOR. Passed, 58–15 (D 36–3; R 22–12), May 5.

Foreign Policy

1941—Lend-Lease. Authorize the President to sell, give, lease or lend materials of war to nations whose defense is deemed vital to

256

the U.S. Lodge FOR. Passed, 60–31 (D 49–13; R 10–17), March 8.

1947—Authorize military and economic assistance to Greece and Turkey. Lodge FOR. Passed, 67–23 (D 32–7; R 35–16), April 22.

1947—Cut interim foreign aid from $597 million to $400 million. Lodge AGAINST. Rejected, 30–56 (D 10–29; R 20–27), Nov. 26.

1948—Economic Cooperation Act of 1948 (Marshall Plan). Lodge FOR. Passed, 69–17 (D 38–4; R 31–13), March 13.

1949—Ratification of North Atlantic Treaty. Lodge FOR. Ratified, 82–13 (D 50–2, R 32–11), July 21.

1949—Korean Aid Act. Lodge FOR. Passed, 48–13 (D 27–7; R 21–6), Oct. 12.

1949—Cut ERP authorization of $5,580,000,000 by 10 percent. Lodge AGAINST. Rejected, 23–54 (D 9–35; R 14–19), April 1.

1949—Amendment to Trade Agreements (Reciprocal Trade) Extension Act to extend act two years from June 30, 1949, instead of three years from June 12, 1948; to retain "peril points" provision of 1948 act; and to require President to give copies of agreements to Congressional finance committees. Lodge FOR. Rejected, 38–43 (D 3–43; R 35–0), Sept. 15.

1949—Foreign Military Assistance Act of 1949, providing arms aid for Atlantic Pact nations. Lodge FOR. Passed, 55–24 (D 36–10; R 19–14), Sept. 22.

1950—Initiate the "technical knowledge and skills" portion of the Point IV program. Lodge FOR. Agreed to, 37–36 (D 29–11; R 8–25), May 5.

1951—Amendment to cut European economic aid from $1,130,500,000 to $880,500,000. Lodge announced AGAINST. Agreed to, 36–34 (D 10–29; R 26–5), Aug. 31.

1952—Reduce mutual security authorization by $200 million. Lodge AGAINST. Agreed to, 37–34 (D 11–24; R 26–7), May 28.

Government Control, States' Rights

1937—A bill granting the President power to enlarge the Supreme Court by appointing six additional justices. Vote on whether to recommit (kill) the bill. Lodge FOR. Agreed to, 70–20 (D 53–18; R 16–0), July 22.

1938—Government Reorganization Act, permitting Presidential reorganizations of Executive agencies to go into effect automatically unless Congress disapproves within 60 days. Lodge AGAINST. Passed, 49–42 (D 47–26; R 0–14), March 28.

1947—Constitutional amendment limiting a President to two terms. Lodge FOR. Passed, 59–23 (D 13–23; R 46–0), March 12.

1951—Parliamentary maneuver to permit speedy consideration of resolution calling for hearings, open to all Senators, on President Truman's recall of Gen. Dougas MacArthur. Lodge FOR. Agreed to, 43–41 (D 1–41; R 42–0), May 2.

Housing

1937—Public Housing Act. Lodge AGAINST. Passed, 64–16 (D 55–8; R 6–8), Aug. 6.

1947—Rent control extension bill. Amendment allowing 15 percent rental increases under certain conditions. Lodge FOR. Agreed to, 48–28 (D 8–24; R 40–2), May 29.

1948—Delete authorization for public housing units from housing bill. Lodge AGAINST. Rejected, 35–49 (D 17–25; R 18–24), April 21.

1949—National Housing Act, providing five-year program of slum clearance and low-cost housing construction. Lodge FOR. Passed, 57–13 (D 33–2; R 24–11), April 21.

1950—Housing Act. Amendment to delete title providing for direct loans to cooperatives through a federal mortgage corporation; and to provide for an assistant commissioner to give technical assistance and advice to cooperatives and nonprofit corporations. Lodge AGAINST. Agreed to, 43–38 (D 13–32; R 30–6), March 15.

1950—Extend federal rent control to Dec. 31, 1950, thereafter on local option only to June 30, 1951. Lodge FOR. Agreed to, 40–24 (D 30–6; R 10–18), June 21.

1951—Independent Offices appropriations. Amendment to authorize 5,000 public housing units instead of 50,000 and appropriate $5 million for such construction rather than $11.4 million. Lodge AGAINST. Rejected, 25–47 (D 7–32; R 18–15), June 20.

LODGE'S STANDS ON KEY ISSUES

Labor

1937—Fair Labor Standards Act, setting a 25-cent-an-hour minimum wage for workers in interstate commerce, to rise to 40 cents in seven years; and, after two years, requiring employers to pay overtime to workers working more than 40 hours a week. Lodge FOR. Passed, 56–28 (D 51–15; R 2–13), July 31.

1943—Smith Connally anti-strike bill, permitting the President to take over struck war plants, providing penalties for instigating a strike in a Government-operated war plant and prohibiting union contributions to political campaigns. Passage over veto. Lodge FOR. Veto overridden, 56–25 (D 29–19; R 27–5), June 25.

1947—Taft-Hartley Act. Amendment to restrict industry-wide bargaining between unions and management. Lodge AGAINST. Rejected, 43–44 (D 12–28; R 3–16), May 7.

1947—Taft-Hartley Act. Amendment permitting both injunctions and damage suits against unions engaging in secondary boycotts or jurisdictional strikes. Lodge AGAINST. Rejected, 28–62 (D 9–34; R 19–28), May 9.

1947—Taft-Hartley Act. Amendment permitting damage suits only against unions engaging in secondary boycotts or jurisdictional strikes. Lodge FOR. Agreed to, 65–26 (D 19–23; R 46–3), May 9.

1947—Taft-Hartley Act. Amendment to outlaw the union shop. Lodge AGAINST. Rejected 21–57 (D 6–28; R 15–29), May 9.

1947—Taft-Hartley Act. Passage over President Truman's veto. Lodge FOR. Veto overridden, 68–25 (D 20–22; R 48–3), June 23.

1949—Delete a labor-bill provision permitting anti-strike injunctions. Lodge FOR. Rejected, 44–46 (D38–14; R 6–32), June 28.

1950—Defense Production Act. Amendment to eliminate selective controls, and to provide that if price controls went into effect, wage controls would also be imposed. Lodge FOR. Agreed to, 50–36 (D 12–34; R 38–2). Aug. 21.

1952—Request that the President immediately invoke the national emergency (injunction) provisions of the Taft-Hartley Act in the steel strike. Lodge announced FOR. Agreed, 49–30 (D 18–27; R 31–3), June 10.

APPENDIX

Resources, Taxes, Economic Policy

1943—Lift the $25,000 ceiling on salaries, established by Executive Order in October 1942, and instead permit salaries up to the maximum paid in the first nine months of 1942. The effect of the proposal was to permit salaries of any amount, provided they did not exceed the January–September 1942 levels. Lodge FOR. Agreed to, 74–3 (D 43–2; R 30–1), March 23.

1947—Increase individual income tax exemption from $500 to $600. Lodge FOR. Rejected, 43–47 (D 33–9; R 10–38), July 15.

1947—Income-tax reduction bill. Passage over veto. Lodge FOR. Two-thirds vote required. Failed to pass, 57–36 (D 10–33; R 47–3), July 18.

1947—Anti-inflation bill. Amendment to permit the President to impose mandatory allocations, priorities and inventory controls on industry, subject to Congresssional disapproval within 30 days. Lodge AGAINST. Rejected. 35–48 (D 31–2; R 1–45), Dec. 18.

1948—Income-tax reduction bill. Passage over veto. Lodge FOR. Veto overridden, 77–10 (D 27–10; R 50–0), April 2.

1948—A bill exempting railroads from antitrust prosecution in some cases. Passage over veto. Lodge FOR. Veto overridden, 63–25 (D 16–22; R 47–3), June 14.

1948—Appropriate $4 million for beginning construction of a TVA steam plant. Lodge AGAINST. Agreed to, 45–37 (D 35–3; R 10–34), June 15.

1948—Anti-inflation bill. Amendment granting President standby rationing and price-wage control authority. Lodge AGAINST. Rejected, 33–53 (D 32–6; R 1–47), Aug. 7.

1949—Reduce electric power funds for Southwestern Power Administration by $2,384,000 and contract authority by $2,742,-000. Lodge FOR. Rejected, 38–45 (D 10–36; R 28–9), Aug. 23.

1950—Exempt independent natural-gas producers from Federal Power Commission jurisdiction. Lodge AGAINST. Passed, 44–38 (D 28–16; R 16–22), March 29.

1950—1951 General Appropriations. Amendment reducing by 10 percent funds appropriated for the Executive Departments, except for defense funds. Lodge FOR. Agreed to, 53–31 (D 19–29; R 36–2), Aug. 3.

1950—Parliamentary maneuver to make Congressional committees report excess-profits tax legislation in the 2nd session of the 81st Congress rather than in the 1st session of the 82nd. Lodge FOR. Rejected, 34–36 (D 23–15; R 11–21), Sept. 14.

1951—Defense Production Act. Amendment prohibiting the Office of Price Stabilization from placing limitations on livestock slaughtering. (The issue was whether or not slaughtering controls were needed to prevent shortages and black market.) Lodge announced AGAINST. Agreed to, 47–33 (D 10–30; R 37–3), June 27.

1951—Cut by $21,393,262 (10 percent) the amount recommended by committee for rivers and harbors. Lodge FOR. Rejected, 38–38 (D 11–32; R 27–6), Aug. 15.

1951—Revenue Act. Instead of applying excess-profits tax to earnings in excess of 75 percent of income, apply the tax to earnings in excess of 85 percent of income. Lodge FOR. Agreed to, 62–20 (D 25–18; R 37–2), Sept. 25.

1952—Agreement between the U.S. and Canada relating to development of Great Lakes-St. Lawrence Basin and providing for making the St. Lawrence seaway self-liquidating. Motion to recommit (kill). Lodge FOR. Bill recommitted, 43–40 (D 19–24; R 24–16), June 18.

1952—Reduce funds for flood control by 10 percent. Lodge announced FOR. Rejected, 27–50 (D 4–36; R 23–14), June 19.

1952—"Tidelands" oil. Transfer from the Federal Government to the states title to lands and their resources (oil) between the low-water mark and the three-mile limit. Lodge announced FOR. Agreed to, 50–35 (D 24–24; R 26–11), April 2.

1952—Delete from Defense Production Act sections extending price and wage controls, thus ending the controls June 30, 1952. Lodge announced AGAINST. Rejected, 18–52 (D 2–40; R 16–12), May 29.

Welfare, Miscellaneous

1947—Confirmation of David E. Lilienthal to head the Atomic Energy Commission. Lodge FOR. Confirmed, 50–31 (D 30–5; R 20–26), April 9.

1948—A bill to cancel Treasury Department regulations expanding Social Security coverage. Passing over veto. Lodge FOR. Veto overridden, 65–12 (D 28–10; R 37–2), June 14.

1950—Internal Security Act. A provision to permit internment of Communists during any "national emergency" if there were "reasonable grounds" for believing they might commit espionage. Amendment to narrow the provision by defining national emergency as consisting only of war, invasion or insurrection. Vote on amendment. Lodge AGAINST. Rejected, 35–37 (D 32–10; R 3–27), Sept. 12.

1950—Internal Security Act. Passage over veto. Lodge FOR. Veto overridden, 57–10 (D 26–10; R 31–0), Sept. 23.

1951—A bill to increase to $120 a month the pensions of veterans requiring constant attendance of other persons because of non-service-connected disabilities. Passage over veto. Lodge FOR. Veto overridden, 69–9 (D 37–7; R 32–2), Sept. 18.

Lodge as a Party Man

Congressional Quarterly's *Party Unity* scores for the 80th Congress and the 81st Congress measure the percentage of roll-call votes on which Lodge voted with the majority of his party. Party Unity scores for the 82nd Congress measure the percentage of times Lodge voted with the majority of his party when it took a stand opposed to the majority of the Democrats.

On the Record scores measure the percentage of times Lodge went on the record on roll-call votes, by voting, pairing or announcing his stand.

Lodge's scores, 1947–52:

| | Party Unity | | |
	Lodge	GOP Average	On the Record
80th Congress (1947–48)	76%		88%
81st Congress (1949–50)	58	76%	86
82nd Congress (1951–52)	56	79	95

Short Biographical Summary

(*New York* Times)

Henry Cabot Lodge

Ambassador to South Vietnam, 1963–64 and 1965–67 . . . now, since June, 1970, President Nixon's special envoy to the Vatican . . . born July 5, 1902, Nahant, Mass. . . . graduated from Harvard, 1924 . . . worked for The Boston Transcript and The New York Herald Tribune . . . two terms in Massachusetts Legislature, 1933–36 . . . defeated James M. Curley for Senate seat, 1936 . . . took leave of absence to serve in Army during World War II . . . won re-election, then resigned from Senate to return to Army duty . . . won Bronze Star, Croix de Guerre, others . . . elected to Senate again, 1946 . . . influential in persuading Eisenhower to seek Presidency and served as his campaign manager . . . lost Senate seat, 1952, to John F. Kennedy . . . appointed U.S. representative at the U.N., 1953 . . . G.O.P. vice-presidential candidate, 1960 . . . chief U.S. negotiator, Paris peace talks, 1969 . . . Ambassador at Large, 1967–68 . . . Ambassador to Germany, 1968–69.

President Kennedy's Exchange with Walter Cronkite Concerning Lodge Appointment as Ambassador to South Vietnam

(*September 5, 1963*)

President Kennedy's appointment of Henry Cabot Lodge as U.S. ambassador to Vietnam provoked some questions by the press. Walter Cronkite, CBS anchorman, asked a question at a White House Press Conference and the following ensued: *

> *Mr. Cronkite:* Mr. President, the sending of Henry Cabot Lodge who after all has been a political enemy of yours over the years at one point or another in your career, and his, sending him out to Saigon might raise some speculation that perhaps you are trying to keep this from being a political issue in 1964.
>
> *President Kennedy:* No. Ambassador Lodge wanted to go out to Saigon. If he were as careful as some politicians are, of course, he would not have wanted to go there. He would have maybe liked to have some safe job, but he is energetic and he has strong feelings about the United States, and surprising as it seems, he put this ahead of his political career. Sometimes politicians do those things, Walter.
>
> *Mr. Cronkite:* Thank you very much, Mr. President.
>
> *President Kennedy:* and we are fortunate to have him.
>
> *Mr. Cronkite:* Thank you, sir. END TEXT

September 5, 1963

* Transcript President's interview contains following differences Verbatim text Reftel: Page 3 PYBAEP* "that would be a great mistake" was repeated.

264

Index

Acheson, Dean, 128, 219
Acheson-Lilienthal proposal, 150
Adams, Brooks, 21
Adams, Henry, 19–21, 173
Adams, John Q., 66
Adams, Sherman, 94, 101, 121, 157n
   Lodge's letter to, 95–97, 98
Addis Ababa (Ethiopia), Lodge's
   visit to, 202–3
Adzubei, Alexis, 162
Agriculture, Lodge's Senate votes on,
   255
Akalovsky, Alexander, 176
Alexander, Herbert, 70n
Alexander III, Czar, 34
Algerian question, 131n, 149
Al-Jamli, Fadil, 139–40
Alsop, Joseph, 56
Anderson, C. Elmer, 124
Appropriations bills, reform of presi-
   dential veto of, 230–31
Aquaviva, Claudio, 130
Aristotle, 21
Aron, Raymond, 205
Ashurst, Henry Fountain, 49–50
Asta, Salvatore, 206
Altantic Institute, Lodge at, 204–5
Atlantic Monthly, 73
Atomic energy, international control
   and developent of, 150
Auspitz, Josiah Lee, 66n

Barco, James W., 130
Baruch, Bernard, 149–50
Baxter, James P., 150
Bell, Jack, 118
Bernstein, Leonard, 220
Berry, Walter, 22n
Bigelow, William Sturgis, 18–19, 25
Birrenbach, Kurt, 205
Bitter Lemons (Durrell), 141
Blair, Clay, on Lodge's vice-presiden-
   tial candidacy, 184

Boston Transcript, Lodge's employ-
   ment at, 29
Bourguiba, Habib, 204
Boyd, Ralph, 107
Bradley, Omar N., 44
Brewster, Owen, 94
Brogan, D. W., 68
Brown, Clarence, 62, 115, 116, 118,
   119
Brownell, Herbert, 80–81, 102, 106–7,
   120
Buddhists in South Vietnam, 207,
   216, 217
Bunau-Varilla, Phillippe, 42–43, 200
Bureaucracy, Hoover Commission re-
   forms and, 62–64
Burke, Edmund, 22
Butler, Ben, 196–97
Byrnes, James F., 55

Cabot, George, 27–28, 67
Cairo, Lodge's visit to, 203–4
Cake, Ralph, 121
Cameron, Martha, 20
Campaign financing, proposal for fed-
   eral funds in, 68–70, 231
Can Can (film), 164, 165
Carey, James B., in exchange with
   Khrushchev, 172
Carlson, Frank, 80, 87n, 96
Carnegie, Andrew, 51
Carney, Leo, 47
Carroll, Michael J., 47
Carter, Amon G., 40
Central Intelligence Agency, 138, 165,
   210
Chevalier, Maurice, 163
Chicago
   1952 Republican Convention in,
     109
   1960 Republican Convention in,
     183
Chicago Tribune, 83

China, Peoples Republic of, 155
Chou En Lai, 177
Churchill, Winston, 98, 224, 247
  on defeat in election of 1945, 188–89n
  United Nations and, 155
  on U.S. Congress, 51–52
Civil rights, 27, 251
  Eisenhower and, 126
  Lodge's proposals for, 73
  Lodge's Senate votes on, 255–56
Civil War, Lodge's ancestors in, 27, 28–29
Clay, Lucius D., Eisenhower presidential candidacy and, 81, 86n, 91, 100, 101, 102, 108, 126
Clayton, William, 205
Cleveland, Grover, 34–35, 66
Cochrane, Jacqueline, 99
Coleman, Thomas, 103, 115, 118, 120
Collective security, 223–24, 226, 249
Columbia University, 77
Conant, James B., 205
Confucianist tradition in Vietnam, 211–12, 216
Congo crisis, 130, 146
Congress
  Coolidge on role of, 32
  problems of, 53–54
  See also Senate
Congressional elections, need for reform of, 229, 230
Constitution, U.S., 232, 233
Coolidge, Calvin, 30–34
Creagen, Geraldine, 85
Crittenberger, Willis D., 43, 58
Cronkite, Walter, on Lodge's appointment to Vietnam, 264
Cuba crisis, 146
cummings, e. e., quoted, 247–48
Curley, James M., 29–30, 47
Cutler, Robert, 121
Cyprus question, 131n, 149
Czechloslovakia, Soviet invasion of, 151

Danang (Vietnam), Struggle Movement in, 216–17
Darby, Harry, 83, 87n
Davis, Charles Henry, 23
Davis, John W., 229
Declaration of Independence, 232, 233
Defense, Lodge's Senate votes on, 256
De Gaulle, Charles, 134
Degradation of the Democratic Dogma, The (Adams), 21
De Lattre, Marshal, 221
Democratic party
  in Massachussetts state legislature, 54–55
  in Senate, 54, 56

1928 Convention of, 38
1932 Convention of, 106–7
De Streel, Helena Lodge, 25n
Devers, Jacob L., 44
Dewey, Thomas, 66, 67, 72, 75, 77, 115, 147, 183
  in Eisenhower draft movement, 80–82, 86n, 120, 122, 239
Diem, Ngo Dinh
  in conversation with Lodge, 207
  overthrow of, 208–10, 212
Dineson, Isak, 199
Dirksen, E. M., 122
Disarmament proposals, 149–50
Disneyland, Khrushchev and, 163–65
Dixon, Pierson, 130–31
Dobrynin, Anatoly F., 144
  letter on Russian-American relations, 145
Dominio de Doriano farm, 200
Don, Tran Van, 214
D'Orlandi, Giovanni, 210n
Douglas, Lewis, 62
Driscoll, Alfred E., 239
Dupuy, R. Ernest, 145
Duff, James H., in Eisenhower draft movement, 79–80, 82, 83, 86n, 95, 96, 120
Dulles, Allen, 138, 165, 166
Dulles, John Foster, 112, 134
  Lebanon crisis and, 138–39
Dunn, Jóhn M., 207
Durrell, Lawrence, 141–42

Early, Stephen, 58
Eastern Europe, Lodge's view on, 249–50
Economic policy, Lodge's Senate votes on, 260–61
Education, Lodge's Senate votes on, 256
Education of Henry Adams, The (Adams), 20
Egypt
  Lodge in, 203–4
  Suez crisis and, 130–31, 133, 135, 136, 137n, 152
Eisenhower, Dwight D., 229
  Abilene speech of, 108–9
  atomic energy program of, 150
  cabinet meetings conducted by, 129–30
  congressional support for candidacy of, 112–13
  defeat of Lodge in 1952 election and, 127
  evaluation of presidency of, 125–26
  intervention in Lebanon ordered by, 138
  Khrushchev's visit to America and, 158, 165
  Korean war policies and, 128

266

on Lodge in 1963, 190, 193
  meeting with Lodge in Paris,
    103–4
  nomination of in 1952, 125
  in presidential campaign of 1952,
    76–126, 237–43
  replies to draft efforts in 1951, 88–
    91, 97–98, 100–101, 104–5
  Suez crisis and, 134
Electoral college system, proposal for
  reform of, 64–68, 228–29

"Fair play" amendment for 1952 Re-
  publican Convention, 107–8,
  112, 114–20
Falkenburg, Jinx, 99
Farley, Jim, 124
Farragut, David G., 28
Fawzi, Mahmoud, 199
Federal Farm Bureau, 32
Federalism, stability of, 51
Fine, John, 102, 110, 239
Flott, Frederick W., 210n
Force Bill, 27
Foreign policy, Lodge's Senate votes
  on, 256–57
Formosa, 135
Ft. Worth Star Telegram, 40
France, Suez crisis and, 130, 134
Franks, Oliver, 205
Freedom of the press
  government secrecy and, 225–26
  Khruschev on, 160
Futility (Gerhardi), 23

Gabrielson, Guy, 87, 110–11, 114
Gad, Ibrahim M., 204
Gardner, Augustus P., 24
Garner, Jack, 54
Garst, Roswell, 175–76
George, Walter, 52–53
Gerhardi, William, 23
Germany, West, Lodge as ambassador
  to, 219–21
Gladwyn, Lord, 205
Glynn, Theodore, 29–30
Goldberg, David, 191, 194
Goldwater, Barry, 190, 192, 194
Goldwyn, Sam, 196
Government control, Lodge's Senate
  votes on, 257–58
Grant, Ulysses S., 28, 29
Great Britain, Suez crisis and, 130–31,
  133, 134
Greece, 148
Grindle, Paul, 191, 194
Gromyko, Andrei, 144, 167
Guatemala, U.S. intervention in, 131
Guggenheim Museum, Lodge's dedi-
  cation address for, 247–48

Habib, Philip C., 222
Hagerty, James, 111–12, 121

Hammarskjold, Dag, 138
  role of UN and, 152–54
Harding, Warren G., 229
Harlem, Khrushchev's visit to, 162–63
Harriman, Averell, 121
Harriman, Edward, 51
Harrison, Benjamin, 66
Harrison, Pat, 56
Harvard College, Lodge at, 24
Hauge, Gabriel, 87
Hay, John, 20
Hayes, Rutherford, 66
Heard, Alexander, 70n
Herman, Ab, 110
Herter, Christian A., 118, 121, 144
Heselton, John, 113
Hickenlooper, Bourke B., 184
Hill, Lester, 78
Hitler, Adolf, 154
Hobby, William P., 103, 106
Hoffman, Paul, 102, 106, 149
Holmes, Oliver Wendell, 244
Honey, Patrick J., 207
Hoover, Herbert, 30–31, 37, 45
  support for Eisenhower candidacy
    by, 113–14
Hoover Commission, 45, 62–64, 230
  government waste revealed by, 63
Horovitz, Samuel B., 46
House of Commons, 53
Housing, Lodge's Senate votes on,
  258
Houston, 1928 Democratic Conven-
  tion in, 38–39
"Houston manifesto," 112
Hubert, Henri, 22n
Hue (Vietnam), Struggle Movement
  in, 216–17
Hungary, Soviet invasion of, 126, 130,
  131, 151

Immigration, Lodge's Senate votes on,
  255–56
India, 137, 151
Indonesia crisis, 149
Ingalls, David, 93, 115, 116–19, 122
Initial Advisory Group in Eisenhower
  campaign, 86
Institute of International Education,
  199
International Longshoremen's Associ-
  ation, 174
Iowa, Khrushchev's visit to, 175–76
Iran, 148
Iraq, 138
Israel, 141
  Suez crisis and, 130, 135, 136, 137n
Ives, Irving, 80

Jackson, Andrew, 66
James, Henry, 24
Japanese diplomats, 146

Jews, in Soviet Union, 167
Johnson, Hiram, 55
Johnson, Lyndon B., 147–48, 214, 219–20
Johnson, Samuel, 196
Jones, Jesse, 39
Jordan, Lebanon crisis and, 138

Kansas City, 1928 Republican Convention in, 38
Kashmir dispute, 131n, 149
Kennan, George, 142
Kennedy, Edward M., 191
Kennedy, John F.
  in election of 1952 for Senate, 125, 127
  instructions to Lodge regarding secrecy, 212–13
  Lodge as ambassador to South Vietnam and, 191, 205, 207
  in presidential election of 1960, 184
Kenya, Lodge in, 200
Khanh, Nguyen, 214
Khrushchev, Nikita, 143
  on American politics, 160
  exchange with Reuther and Carey, 172
  on freedom of the press, 160
  on labor, 171–72
  on private property, 173–74
  on Suez crisis, 137n
  visit to America by, 126, 157–81
    Disneyland affair, 163–65
    Harlem, 162–63
    Iowa, 175–76
    Los Angeles, 163–68
    San Francisco, 171–74
    San Luis Obispo incident, 170
    Santa Barbara, 169–70
    whistle stop tour, 168–70
    "we will bury you" speech, 166–67
Khrushchev in America, 178
Khrushchev Remembers (Khrushchev), 137n
Knowland, William F., 115–16, 117, 119, 239
Knox, Philander C., 42–43
Korean war, 76, 129, 148, 226
  prisoner of war policies in, 128
  UN and, 154–55
Krock, Arthur, 69
Kuznetsov, Vasily V., 254
Ky, Nguyen Cao, 215, 217

Labor legislation, 46, 56
  Lodge's Senate votes on, 259
LaFollette, Robert M., 38
Langlie, Arthur B., 118
Lapsley, Gaillard, 23
Larmon, Sigurd, 87, 99–100
Lawrence, William, 19
League of Nations

compared with United Nations, 250
H. C. Lodge, Sr., on, 27
Leahy, William D., 58
Lease, Mary Ellen, 52
Lebanon crisis, 137–41
  U.S. intervention in, 126, 130, 138
Liberia, 135
Libya, Lodge in, 57
Life magazine, 189
Lincoln, Abraham, 27, 29, 196
Lindbergh, Charles A., 30–31
Lloyd, Selwyn, 134
Lodge, Emily Sears (wife), 30, 200
Lodge, George (son), 191
Lodge, Henry Cabot, Jr.
  in Africa, 200–204
    in Addis Ababa, 202–3
    in Cairo, 203
    in Kenya, 200–202
    in Sudan, 203
    in Tunisia, 204
  as ambassador to Germany, 219–21
  as ambassador to South Vietnam, 189, 191, 205–19
    building of new embassy building, 218–19
    conversations with Diem, 207
    disposal of Diem, 208–9, 212
    Kennedy and, 191, 205, 207
    Kennedy's instructions regarding secrecy, 212–13
    mistaken charges of Pentagon Papers, 209–11, 213
    resignation of in 1964, 214
    view of Vietnam problem, 205–6
  ancestors of, 27–29
  at Atlantic Institute, 204–5
  as chairman of Institute of International Education, 199
  childhood of, 17–24
  as consultant for Time, Inc., 189
  in draft movement of Eisenhower in 1952 presidential campaign, 75–126
    chosen as campaign manager, 83–85
    letter to Adams on entering Eisenhower in primary, 95–97, 98
    meeting with Eisenhower in Paris, 103–4
    replies by Eisenhower to draft movement, 88–91, 97–98, 100–101, 104–5
    at San Francisco meeting, 93
  education of
    at Harvard College, 24
    at Middlesex School, 24
    in Paris, 23
  in Eisenhower administration transitional duities, 128–29
  as envoy to Vatican, 222

268

Guggenheim Museum dedication
  address of, 247–48
journalistic career of, 29–42, 45
in Nicaragua, 41–42
with Khrushchev in America, 157–
  81
in Massachusetts state legislature,
  labor legislation, 46
military service of
  in army reserve, 43–45, 57
  in World War II, 57–59
in New Hampshire presidential
  primary of 1964, 189–94
in Paris as representative to Vietnam peace talks, 221–22
Republican party and
  modernization proposals, 72–73,
    253
  platform adopted by 1948 Con-
    vention, 70–72, 78
  Senate voting record as party
    man, 262
  See also Republican party
as Republican vice-presidential
  candidate in 1960, 146, 183
  description of campaign life, 185–
    88
  role of television in, 184
in Senate, 49–75
  defeat in 1952 election, 127
  election of 1936, 47
  election of 1946, 61
  electoral reform proposal, 64–68,
    228–29
  on Foreign Relations Committee,
    61
  Hoover Commission sponsored,
    62
  as party man, 262
  resignation from for military
    service, 57
  Social Security amendment, 55
  visit to war theaters, 57
  voting record, 255–62
in United Nations as U.S. representative, 129–55, 184–85
  Congo crisis, 146
  Lebanon crisis, 138–41
  replies to Soviet charges, 253–54
  Suez crisis, 130–37
  Tibet question, 254
  U-2 incident, 143–44, 146, 254
  See also United Nations
West Point graduation address of,
  244–46
Lodge, Henry Cabot, Sr. (grand-
  father), 17, 25–27
  Force Bill and, 27
  Theodore Roosevelt and, 21
Lodge, John Davis (brother), 20n, 25,
  112
Lodge, Mathilda (mother), 25, 29

Lovett, Robert, 62
Lowden, Frank, 229
Loyalty investigations, 251–52
Luce, Henry R., 189

McAdoo, William G., 229
MacArthur, Douglas, 242
  dismissal of, 250
  keynote speech at 1952 Republican
    Convention, 118, 120
McCarthy, Joseph, 126
McCormick, Robert, 83, 123
McCoy, Frank R., 41–42
McCrary, Tex, 98–99
McKeldin, Theodore, 108, 238–43
MacLeish, Archibald, 18
MacMillan, Harold, 142
McNamara, Robert S., on Lodge's
  role in Vietnam, 213–14
McNary, Charles L., 52
Mailer, Norman, 85
Making of the President: 1960, The
  (White), 184n
Maldive Islands, 151
Marshall, George C., 44, 57–58, 61,
  226
  defeat of Lodge in 1952 election
    and, 128
Marshall Plan, 61–62, 149, 226, 232
Mattingly, Barak, in draft Eisen-
  hower movement, 82–83, 87n,
  117–18, 120
Mau Mau movement, 200
Mencken, Henry L., 40–41
Menon, Krishna, 136, 137
Menshikov, Mikhail A., 162–64, 166–
  68, 174
Metternich, C. L. W. (Prince), 220–21
Meyer, Eugene, 31–32
Meyers, Harold B., 70n
Mickelson, Sig, 70n, 122n
Middlesex School, Lodge at, 24
Milliken, Eugene D., 61
Mind of the President, The (Slemp),
  32
Minh, Duong Van, 214
Monroe, Marilyn, 163
Mont St. Michel and Chartres
  (Adams), 20
Montaigne, Michel, 18, 244
Montgomery, Bernard L., 44
Morgan, J. P., 38, 51
Moses, George H., 37, 52
Muniz, Joao Carlos, 132
Mutual security, 223–24, 226

Nahant (Mass.), Lodge's summers at,
  25–26
Nakayama, Riri, 19
Nasser, Gamal, 203
National Security Council, 130

269

NATO (North Atlantic Treaty Organization), 77–78, 103, 135
Natural resources, Lodge's Senate votes on, 260–61
Negroes, protection of suffrage for, 27
Nehru, Pandit, 137, 166
New Hampshire
  Lodge's "candidacy" in 1964 primary in, 189–94
  primary of 1952 in, 22n, 93–102, 108
New York *Herald-Tribune*, 94
  Lodge's employment at, 29, 30, 35
Newberry, Cammann, 185
Newsom, Earl, 87
Newspapers, political views of in 1952 Republican presidential contest, 237–38
Nhu, Ngo Dinh, 207, 210n
Nhu, Madam Ngo Dinh, 207
Nicaragua, Lodge in, 41–42
Niven, David, 163
Nixon, Richard M., 66n, 239
  arms limitation agreements and, 150
  foreign policy of, 227–28
  guaranteed income proposal of, 231
  Lodge chosen as vice-presidential candidate by, 183
  Paris peace talk appointment for Lodge, 221
  in presidential campaign of 1960, 183, 188
  Vatican appointment for Lodge, 222
Norton, Robert, 23
Nyeri reservation, Lodge at, 201–2

O'Brien, Robert Lincoln, 34
O'Brien, Vincent P., 187
Olvaney, George W., 39–40
Out of Africa (Dineson), 199

Pakistan, conflict of with East Pakistan, 151
Paris
  education of Lodge in, 23
  Lodge at Vietnam peace talks in, 221–22
Patton, George S., 44–45, 76
Pearson, Lester B., 132–33, 205
Penrose, Boies, 38
Pentagon Papers, mistaken allegations in, 209–11, 213
Pericles, quoted, 245–46
Persons, Wilton B., 157n
Pétain, Henri Philippe, 43
Peterson, Howard, 86
Philadelphia, Republican Convention of 1948 in, 70–72, 78
Philippines, 135
Pierce, Franklin, 195–96

Plato, 50
Politicians, attitude of public toward, 194–96
Porter, David D., 28
Poverty, elimination of, 231
Presidential appointments, 231
Presidential campaigns, proposal for public financing of, 68–70, 231
Presidential elections
  need for reform of, 64–68, 228
  nominating procedure reforms for, 228–29, 230
Presidential powers, 250
Propaganda war, 227

Rabb, Maxwell M., 85, 124, 129n
Rahman el Tohany, Abdel, 203
Reconstruction Finance Corporation, 39
Reece, Brazilla Carroll, 118
Reed, James A., 36–37
Religion in politics, 252
Renno, R. F., Jr., 129n
Republican party
  affiliation of Lodge with, 27
  conservatives in, 190–91
  draft Eisenhower movement in, 76–126
  electoral reform bill opposed by, 67–68
  "fair play" amendment for, 107–8, 112, 114
  isolationists in, 77, 79
  modernization proposals for, 72–73, 253
  in Senate, 54–55, 56, 62
  Taft's analysis of 1952 presidential candidacy, 237–43
  1928 Convention of, 38
  1948 Convention platform of, 70–72, 78
  1952 Convention of, 109
  1952 New Hampshire primary of, 22n, 93–102, 108
  1952 Texas state convention of, 105–6, 111, 115
  1960 Convention of, 183
  1964 New Hampshire primary of, 189–94
Reuther, Walter P., in exchange with Khrushchev, 172
Review of Politics, The (journal), 189
Revolutionary wars, need for protection against, 226–27
Richardson, Henry H., 20
Robinson, William A., 94
Rocco, M. M., 200
Rockefeller, John D., 51
Rockefeller, Nelson, in New Hampshire primary of 1964, 190, 192, 193, 194

Rogers, Kenneth, 210n
Rogers, Will, 69
Roosevelt, Franklin D., 47, 49, 154, 229
  "Happy Warrior" speech of, 39
  Lodge's military service and, 58–59
  victory at 1932 Democratic Convention, 106–7
Roosevelt, Theodore, 21–22, 41–43
  campaign financing and, 69
Rovere, Richard, 126, 155
Rueff, Jacques, 205
Rusk, Dean, 204, 215

Said, Nuri, 138
Saltonstall, Leverett, 46
Saltonstall, Sally, 191
San Francisco
  Khrushchev's visit to, 171–74
  Republican meeting of 1952 in, 93
Santa Barbara (California), Khrushchev's visit to, 169–70
Saturday Evening Post, 56, 186
Scott, Hugh, 107, 112–13
Scott, R. F., 244
Scranton, William W., 214
Sears, Henry, 86
Sears, Mason, 80, 85, 108
Secrecy in government, 225–26
Senate
  election reform for, 229, 230
  Foreign Relations Committee, 52, 61
  individualists in, 53
  Lodge in, 49–75
  See also Lodge, Henry Cabot, in Senate
  positive characteristics of, 73–74
  Social Security debate in, 55
  unique feature of, 50–51
  See also Congress
Separation of powers, 32
Sherwood, Philip, 43
Sherwood, Robert, 43
Simonds, Frank H., 42
Simpson, "Jerry," 51–52
Sisco, Joseph J., 132
Slemp, C. Bascom, 32–33
Smith, Al, 39, 196, 229
Smoot, Reed, 38
Sobolev, Arkady, 140, 144
Social Security Act, Senate debate over, 55
Soviet Union
  expansionism of, 223, 250–51
  invasion of Czechoslovakia by, 151
  invasion of Hungary by, 126, 130, 131, 151
  Jews in, 167
  Korean war and, 155
  Lebanon crisis and, 141

relations of with U.S., 144–45, 227–28
  spying on American Embassy by, 142–43
  U-2 incident and, 143–44, 146, 254
Spaak, Paul Henri, 133–35, 205
Sprague, J. Russel, 87n, 120
Stalin, Josef, 174–75, 223, 226
Stassen, Harold, 99, 238–43
States' rights, Lodge's Senate votes on, 257–58
Stephens, Thomas, 80, 85, 87n, 99
Struggle Movement in South Vietnam, 216–18
Sudan, Lodge in, 203
Suez crisis of 1956, 126, 130–37
  Spaak amendment and, 133–35
  United Nations and, 130–37
Sukhodrov, Viktor M., 176
Sulzberger, C. L., 98
Summerfield, Arthur, 102, 103, 110, 239
Supreme Court
  Coolidge on role of, 32
  court packing proposal for, 49–50
Syria, Lebanon crisis and, 138

Taft, Robert A., 59, 61, 72, 190, 229
  analysis of 1952 Republican presidential contest, 237–43
  "Houston manifesto" and, 113
  on Lodge in the UN, 129n
  in New Hampshire primary of 1952, 93–94, 99
  popularity of, 75–77
  presidential primary of 1952 and, 75–79, 83, 108–23
  on Texas state convention of 1952, 106, 107
Talbott, Harold, 86
Tammany Hall, 39
Tarnoff, Peter, 222
Tax revision proposal, 73
Taxes, Lodge's Senate votes on, 260–61
Taylor, Maxwell D., 214
Television
  Lodge's poplarity and, 184
  use of in 1952 campaign, 122
Terrar, Edward F., 188
Terrorist wars, need for protection against, 226–27
Tet offensive (1968), 218–19
Texas, Republican state convention of 1952 in, 105–6, 111, 115
Thailand, 135
Thi, Nguyen Chanh, 216
Thieu, Nguyen Van, 215
Thomas Aquinas, 20
Thompson, Llewellyn, 171
Thornton, Daniel, 112
Thurber, Henry T., 34–36

271

Thurmond, Strom, 66
Thye, Ed, 124
Tibet question, 254
Tilden, Samuel, 66
Tillman, Ben, 51
Time (magazine), 30
Tokyo, Lodge in, 19
Toynbee, Arnold, 141
Traugott, John P., 189
Triumph and Tragedy (Churchill), 188n
Trowt, John A., 46
Trueheart, William C., 206
Truman, Harry S., 61–62, 66, 67, 75, 150, 154
  Korean war policy of, 128
  presidential campaign of 1952 and, 78
  on Republican platform of 1948, 71–72
Truman Doctrine, 226
Tunisia, Lodge in, 204

U Thant, 137n
U-2 plane incident, 143–44, 146, 254
Ulysses, 223
Unfinished Struggles (Spaak), 134
United Nations
  anticolonialism in, 149
  atomic energy programs of, 150
  Congo crisis and, 146
  Development Program of, 149
  different from League of Nations, 250
  disarmament and, 149–50
  Emergency Force of, 131, 135–37
  evaluation of record of, 148–55
  Hammarskjold and, 152–54
  Lebanon crisis and, 137–41
  Lodge appointed representative to, 129
  need for hospitality in, 146–47
  "nonaligned" ("neutralist") nations in, 136
  priorities of, 149
  purpose of, 224–25
  Security Council of, 131, 139
  Suez crisis and, 131–37
  Tibet question and, 254
  U.S. allies in, 135
  U-2 incident, 143–44, 146, 254
  Vietnam problems and, 150–51

Valletta, Vittorio, 205
Vandenberg, Arthur, 52, 84, 87n
Vanderbilt, Cornelius, 51
Vasilew, Eugene, on Lodge in New Hampshire primary of 1964, 189–94
Veto power, reform of, 230–31
Vicksburg, Civil War battle at, 28–29
Viet Cong, 216, 218–19

Vietnam, North
  as authoritarian state, 212
  propaganda of, 227
Vietnam, South, 126
  American embassy in, 218–19
  Catholics in, 206–7
  Confucianist tradition in, 211–12, 216
  coup against Diem in, 208–9, 212
  lack of democratic tradition in, 211–12, 215
  Lodge at Paris peace talks and, 221–22
  need for constitution in, 215–16
  political instability in, 214–15
  Struggle Movement in, 216–18
  Tet offensive in, 218–19
  United Nations and, 150–51, 206
  war against communism in, 206
Vishinsky, Andrei, 129, 253–54

Wadsworth, James J., 147
Wallace, Henry A., 67
Warren, Earl, 108, 110, 238–43
Washington Post, 32
Watson, "Jim," 56
Weeks, Sinclair, 47, 121
Welfare proposals, 252–53
  Lodge's Senate votes on, 261–62
Wellington, Arthur, Duke of, 188
West Point, Lodge's graduation address at, 244–46
Wharton, Edith, 22–23
Wheeler, Wayne B., 36
Whistler, George Washington, 145
Whistler, James, 145
White, Theodore H., 184n
White, Thomas W., 47, 124
Whitney, John H., 86
Wiley, Alexander, 61
Wilhelm II, Kaiser, 154
Williams, Carolyn, 191
Williams, James T., Jr., 29
Williams, Walter, 102
Willkie, Wendell, 56, 84
Wood, Leonard, 41, 229
World War I, 154, 226
World War II, 44–45, 154, 226, 227
  lessons of, 223
  Lodge's service in, 22n, 57–59
  military strength necessitated by, 56–57
  North African campaign, 45
  Taft's record in, 75
Wright, Frank Lloyd, 247
Wright, John, 222

Yeats, W. B., 232

Zakharov, Nikolay S., 164, 170
Zeeland, Paul van, 205
Zhukov, Georgiy A., 164

361678

R00008 32075

B LODGE 361678 7.50

LODGE

STORM HAS MANY EYES

ATLANTA PUBLIC LIBRARY